DYSPHAGIA
COOKBOOK

Copyright

Disclaimer

The recipes and information in this cookbook are intended for informational purposes only and are not a substitute for professional medical advice. Always consult a healthcare professional to ensure that the dietary needs of the individual with dysphagia are met.

The author and publisher are not liable for any harm from the use of the information and recipes in this book. While efforts have been made to ensure the accuracy of the information, no warranty is provided. The author and publisher will not be liable for any errors, omissions, or inaccuracies in this book or for any adverse effects arising from its use.

TABLE OF CONTENTS

PREFACE

Introduction to Dysphagia

Welcome to this comprehensive guide crafted to enhance the quality of life for those with dysphagia. This cookbook aims to bridge the gap between strict dietary requirements and the pleasure of eating.

Purpose of the Cookbook

This cookbook is carefully tailored for anyone involved in care—whether you're a health professional, a loving family member, or someone personally experiencing dysphagia. My aim is to simplify the process of meal preparation, focusing on IDDSI levels 4 (pureed), 5 (minced and moist), and 6 (soft and bite-sized). Each recipe has been thoughtfully developed to ensure it's safe, easy to swallow, and nutritionally beneficial, all while being flavorful and visually appealing.

Your Feedback Matters

Your thoughts are incredibly valuable. Sharing your feedback not only helps others discover and benefit from this resource, but it also encourages me to continue creating delicious and nutritious recipes for the dysphagia community. If this cookbook has been helpful to you, please take a moment to scan the QR code below and leave a review.

CHAPTER 1: UNDERSTANDING DYSPHAGIA

What is Dysphagia?

Dysphagia is a condition characterized by difficulty in swallowing. Those affected may struggle with swallowing certain types of food or liquids, leading to possible malnutrition, dehydration, and more serious complications like aspiration pneumonia. Effective management of dysphagia is vital to maintain a good quality of life and ensure safe, adequate nutrition.

Causes and Diagnosis

Dysphagia can be caused by a variety of health conditions, each affecting the swallowing process in different ways. Some of the most common causes include:

- **Neurological Disorders:** Conditions like stroke, Parkinson's disease, multiple sclerosis, and cerebral palsy can disrupt the brain's control over swallowing.
- **Head and Neck Cancers:** Tumors in the mouth, throat, or esophagus can physically obstruct or damage swallowing structures.
- **Structural Changes:** Injuries or surgeries to the head, neck, or chest area can alter the anatomy necessary for proper swallowing.
- **Degenerative Diseases:** Progressive conditions such as Alzheimer's disease or ALS (Amyotrophic Lateral Sclerosis) gradually impair the muscles and nerves governing swallowing.
- **Infections and Inflammations:** Conditions like esophagitis can cause swelling and irritation in the esophagus, making swallowing painful.

Diagnosing dysphagia typically involves a combination of medical history evaluation, physical examinations, and specialized tests. Key diagnostic procedures include:

- **Swallowing Assessment:** Performed by a speech-language pathologist, this evaluation tests the safety and efficiency of swallowing using different consistencies of food and liquid.
- **Barium Swallow X-ray:** This imaging test involves swallowing a barium-containing liquid that coats the lining of the esophagus, stomach, and intestines, making them visible on an X-ray to detect abnormalities.
- **Endoscopy:** Using a flexible tube with a light and camera (endoscope) to view the throat and esophagus directly.
- **Manometry:** Measures the rhythmic muscle contractions, coordination, and force exerted by the esophagus during swallowing.
- **Fiberoptic Endoscopic Evaluation of Swallowing (FEES):** A procedure that uses a small camera passed through the nose to observe swallowing mechanisms directly.

CHAPTER 2:
THE IDDSI FRAMEWORK

Overview of IDDSI Levels 6, 5, and 4

The International Dysphagia Diet Standardisation Initiative (IDDSI) provides a global standard for food textures and drink thicknesses, ensuring safety and nutritional adequacy for those with dysphagia. Here, I focus on Levels 6, 5, and 4, each tailored to specific swallowing needs.

Level 6: Soft and Bite-Sized

- **Description:** Food at this level is soft, moist, and easily mashed with gentle pressure. It should be no larger than 0.6in for adults, making it easy to chew and swallow.
- **Examples:** Soft-boiled vegetables, tender meats, and soft, flaky fish.

IDDSI offers a comprehensive guide with visual demonstrations and detailed explanations of testing methods and food textures, accessible via the QR code below:

Level 5: Minced and Moist

- **Description:** Foods are moist and minced into small pieces no larger than 0.1in for adults. This texture is cohesive enough to scoop and hold together on a spoon.
- **Examples:** Minced chicken with gravy, mashed potatoes with butter, or soft fruit compote.

IDDSI offers a comprehensive guide with visual demonstrations and detailed explanations of testing methods and food textures, accessible via the QR code below:

Level 4: Pureed

- **Description**: Foods are pureed to a smooth, consistent texture. They should not require chewing and should not form any lumps.
- **Examples:** Pureed fruits, vegetables, and meats, smooth soups, and smoothies.

IDDSI offers a comprehensive guide with visual demonstrations and detailed explanations of testing methods and food textures, accessible via the QR code below:

CHAPTER 3: GETTING STARTED IN THE KITCHEN

This chapter is designed to equip caregivers, family members, and individuals dealing with dysphagia with the essential knowledge and tools needed to prepare safe, nutritious, and appealing meals. Here I cover the necessary kitchen equipment, dining aids, cooking tips for texture modification, and guidance on which ingredients to avoid or modify.

Essential Tools and Equipment

Preparing meals for someone with dysphagia requires a few key kitchen tools that help in modifying textures to meet IDDSI standards. The following tools are:

- **Blender or Food Processor:** Crucial for creating purees and smooth liquids, a high-quality blender can handle everything from fruits and vegetables to meats.
- **Fine Mesh Sieve:** Useful for straining purees and soups to ensure they are free of lumps and perfectly smooth.
- **Electric Mixer:** Helps in achieving the right texture for mashed foods and in blending ingredients to the desired consistency.
- **Steamer Basket:** Excellent for cooking a variety of foods, including vegetables, proteins, and even items traditionally baked. It cooks food evenly with steam, preserving nutrients and maintaining the food's shape and texture.
- **Silicone Food Mold:** By shaping pureed or soft foods into appealing shapes, these molds enhance the visual appeal of meals, promote dignity, and stimulate the appetite.
- **Kitchen Scales:** Essential for measuring ingredients accurately to ensure consistency in recipe results, which is important for maintaining nutritional balance.
- **Knives and Cutting Boards:** A set of sharp knives and separate cutting boards for produce, meat, and bread can help prevent cross-contamination.
- **Cooking Utensils:** Rubber spatulas, whisks, and ladles are helpful for mixing, stirring, and serving.

Dining Aids for Dysphagia

Eating independently can be challenging for individuals with dysphagia. Specialized dining aids can make mealtime safer and more enjoyable, allowing those affected to eat more independently. Here are some essential tools:

- **Adaptive Cutlery:** Lightweight or angled cutlery can help individuals who have limited dexterity or control. Cutlery with larger, non-slip handles can also be easier to grip.
- **Non Slip Mats:** Placing a non slip mat under plates or bowls can prevent them from sliding, making it easier to eat with one hand.
- **Plate Guards:** These are raised edges that attach to the rim of a plate to help in scooping food onto utensils, beneficial for those with coordination difficulties.
- **Scoop Bowls and Plates:** These have one side that is higher than the other, aiding in scooping food onto utensils without spilling.

- **Special Cups:** Cups with cut-out rims, nosey cups, or cups with lids and spouts can help control the flow of liquids and reduce the risk of choking or aspiration. These are particularly useful for those who have difficulty tilting their heads back.

Tips for Cooking and Texture Modification

Modifying the texture of food is key in preparing meals for those with swallowing difficulties. Here are some effective techniques:

- **Gradual Addition of Liquids:** When creating purees or minced textures, add liquids slowly to achieve the desired consistency without making the dish too watery.
- **Temperature Control:** Cooking ingredients at the right temperature can help maintain their nutritional value while making them easier to puree or mash.
- **Consistency Testing:** Regularly use the IDDSI testing methods to ensure that the food texture aligns with the appropriate IDDSI level.
- **Use of Thickeners:** When necessary, employ commercial thickeners to adjust the viscosity of liquids or semi-liquids to prevent choking.

Ingredients to Avoid or Modify Based on the Underlying Illness

When managing dysphagia, it's important to consider the underlying cause of the condition, as this can affect dietary restrictions and needs. Here are some common conditions associated with dysphagia and the specific types of foods that may need to be avoided or modified:

- **Stroke:** Patients recovering from a stroke may struggle with weakened swallowing reflexes and muscle control. It's best to avoid foods that are hard to chew or could lead to choking, such as tough meats, whole fruits, or chunky soups. Smooth, uniform textures are usually safer and easier to handle.
- **Gastroesophageal Reflux Disease (GERD):** Those with GERD need to avoid acidic and spicy foods that can irritate the esophagus and exacerbate symptoms. Common trigger foods include citrus fruits (like lemons), tomatoes, chocolate, mint, and foods high in fat.
- **Parkinson's Disease:** Parkinson's can lead to difficulties in both the mechanical and coordination aspects of swallowing. Dry or crumbly foods such as breads and cookies can be particularly challenging, as well as foods that are too slippery, like whole pieces of certain fruits. Soft, moist foods that require minimal effort for chewing and swallowing are recommended.
- **Multiple Sclerosis (MS):** MS can cause a wide range of swallowing difficulties depending on the nerves affected. Foods that are too hot or too cold can trigger dysphagia symptoms, and foods that crumble easily or have mixed textures (e.g., cereal with milk) may also be difficult to manage. Consistent textures that are easy to control in the mouth are recommended.
- **Esophageal Cancer:** For those undergoing treatment for esophageal cancer, inflamed or narrowed areas of the esophagus can make swallowing painful and difficult. Soft, smooth, and creamy foods like yogurt, pureed fruits, and soups are preferable to avoid irritation. Spicy, acidic, and rough-textured foods should be avoided.
- **Neurological Disorders:** For individuals with conditions such as ALS (amyotrophic lateral sclerosis) or Huntington's disease, avoiding foods that require complex mouth movements or are choking hazards is crucial. Small, hard foods like nuts, seeds, and popcorn, and very sticky or stringy foods, like caramel and fibrous fruits and vegetables, should be modified or avoided.

CHAPTER 4:
IDDSI LEVEL 6 RECIPES
(SOFT AND BITE-SIZED)

SAVORY PARMESAN OATS WITH THYME AND OLIVE OIL

TOTAL TIME: 30 minutes	CALORIES: 602	SERVINGS: 1	CARBS: 34g	PROTEIN: 21g	FATS: 43g

INGREDIENTS:

- 1/3 cup large oat flakes
- 6 tablespoons grated Parmesan cheese
- 1 small onion
- 2 medium button mushrooms
- 1 clove garlic
- 4 sprigs fresh thyme
- 2 tablespoons olive oil
- 300ml chicken broth
- 1 teaspoon unsalted butter
- Salt and pepper to taste
- 2 tablespoons whole milk
- 50ml water

INSTRUCTIONS:

1. Finely chop onion and mushrooms into 0.6in pieces; mince garlic; sauté in olive oil over medium heat for 5 minutes; add oat flakes; stir for 2 minutes; add broth and water; simmer for 10 minutes; stir in thyme leaves; cook for 5 minutes.
2. Remove from heat; stir in Parmesan cheese, butter and milk; season with salt and pepper to taste.

TENDER TURKEY, APPLE AND ONION HASH

TOTAL TIME: 20 minutes	CALORIES: 702	SERVINGS: 1	CARBS: 35g	PROTEIN: 40g	FATS: 46g

INGREDIENTS:

- 200g ground turkey
- 1 medium apple
- 1 medium onion
- 2 tablespoons olive oil
- Salt and pepper to taste
- 1/2 teaspoon dried thyme
- 1/4 teaspoon garlic powder
- 50ml chicken broth

INSTRUCTIONS:

1. Peel and dice the apple and onion into 0.6in pieces; heat olive oil in a pan over medium heat; add onion; cook for 3 minutes; add ground turkey; cook, breaking it into small pieces, for 5 minutes; stir in apple, thyme, garlic powder, salt, and pepper; cook for 5 minutes.
2. Pour in chicken broth; simmer for 7 minutes; season with salt and pepper to taste.

SMOKED SALMON, EGG AND AVOCADO MASH SANDWICH

TOTAL TIME: 10 minutes	CALORIES: 357	SERVINGS: 1	CARBS: 26g	PROTEIN: 16g	FATS: 21g

INGREDIENTS:

- 2 slices whole wheat bread
- 1 large egg
- 1/4 ripe avocado
- 1 ounce smoked salmon
- 1 tablespoon mayonnaise
- Milk or stock

INSTRUCTIONS:

1. Boil the egg, let sit covered in hot water for 9-12 minutes, then cool, peel, and finely mash.
2. Pulse bread in a food processor to fine crumbs (<0.1in).
3. In a square mould on a plate, add half the breadcrumbs. Moisten with milk or stock.
4. Combine mashed egg and mayonnaise. Add smooth mashed avocado and chopped salmon (0.6in pieces). Mix to a uniform, moist filling.
5. Fill mould with the mixture, top with remaining breadcrumbs, and moisten again.
6. Cover and refrigerate for 1 hour to set; remove from mould and cut into pieces.

CREAMY COCONUT AND PINEAPPLE RICE

TOTAL TIME: 25 minutes	CALORIES: 984	SERVINGS: 1	CARBS: 97g	PROTEIN: 13g	FATS: 63g

INGREDIENTS:

- 1/2 cup short-grain rice
- 200ml coconut milk
- 1/2 cup pineapple, fresh or canned
- 1 tablespoon coconut oil
- 1/4 teaspoon salt
- 1/2 teaspoon sugar
- 100ml water

INSTRUCTIONS:

1. If using fresh pineapple, peel, core, and chop the fruit. Purée it in a blender. If using canned pineapple, ensure it is drained and then puréed.
2. Rinse rice under cold water until the water runs clear.
3. In a pot, combine rinsed rice, coconut milk, water, and salt; bring to a boil; reduce heat to low; cover and simmer for 15 minutes; stir in the pineapple purée.

SCRAMBLED EGGS WITH MELTED CHEESE AND PUREED SPINACH

TOTAL TIME: 15 minutes	CALORIES: 384	SERVINGS: 1	CARBS: 4g	PROTEIN: 21g	FATS: 33g

INGREDIENTS:

- 2 large eggs
- 1/4 cup shredded cheddar cheese
- 2 cups fresh spinach
- Salt and pepper to taste
- 1 tablespoon olive oil

INSTRUCTIONS:

1. Heat 1 tablespoon of olive oil in a pan over medium heat; cook 2 cups of fresh spinach for 5 minutes; puree.
2. Beat 2 large eggs in a bowl, season with salt and pepper, then add to the same pan; sprinkle 1/4 cup of shredded cheddar cheese over them; mix well until combined.

SOFT BLUEBERRY AND COTTAGE CHEESE PANCAKES

TOTAL TIME: 30 minutes	CALORIES: 430	SERVINGS: 1	CARBS: 52g	PROTEIN: 26g	FATS: 14g

INGREDIENTS:

- 1/2 cup all-purpose flour
- 1/2 cup cottage cheese
- 1/4 cup blueberries
- 1 large egg
- 1 tablespoon milk

INSTRUCTIONS:

1. Blend flour, cottage cheese, egg, and milk until smooth; fold in mashed or pureed blueberries.
2. Heat a non-stick pan over low heat to avoid crust formation.
3. Pour batter into the pan for smaller pancakes; cook on very low heat for approximately 6 minutes and cover to steam-cook, preventing browning.

ZUCCHINI AND BELL PEPPER SOFT SCRAMBLE

TOTAL TIME: 20 minutes	CALORIES: 304	SERVINGS: 1	CARBS: 6g	PROTEIN: 13g	FATS: 24g

INGREDIENTS:

- 2 large eggs
- 1/2 cup zucchini
- 1/2 cup red bell pepper
- 1 tablespoon olive oil
- Salt and pepper to taste

INSTRUCTIONS:

1. Heat the olive oil in a pan over medium heat; add the grated zucchini and the chopped bell pepper; cook for 7 minutes.
2. Beat the eggs with salt and pepper, then pour them over the soft vegetables in the pan.
3. Stir gently, cooking until the eggs are set but very soft.

TENDER SHAKSHUKA

TOTAL TIME: 30 minutes	CALORIES: 318	SERVINGS: 1	CARBS: 14g	PROTEIN: 14g	FATS: 24g

INGREDIENTS:

- 2 large eggs
- 1 cup canned crushed tomatoes
- 1/4 cup red bell pepper
- 1/4 cup onion
- 1 garlic clove
- 1 tablespoon olive oil
- 1/2 teaspoon paprika
- Salt and pepper to taste

INSTRUCTIONS:

1. Heat the olive oil in a pan on low; add the pureed onion, bell pepper, and garlic; cook for 15 minutes.
2. Mix in the crushed tomatoes and paprika; simmer for 10 minutes; season with salt and pepper.
3. On low heat, blend the beaten eggs into the sauce; cook until eggs are set but tender.

CREAMY POLENTA WITH ROASTED TOMATOES

TOTAL TIME: 30 minutes	CALORIES: 466	SERVINGS: 1	CARBS: 47g	PROTEIN: 22g	FATS: 21g

INGREDIENTS:

- 1/2 cup polenta
- 1 cup whole milk
- 1/2 cup cherry tomatoes
- 1 teaspoon olive oil
- 1/4 cup grated Parmesan cheese
- Salt and pepper to taste

INSTRUCTIONS:

1. Heat the oven to 375°F; toss the cherry tomatoes with olive oil, salt, and pepper on a baking sheet; bake for 20 minutes.
2. Bring 1 cup of whole milk to a boil. Whisk in the polenta, reduce the heat, and stir for 5 minutes.
3. Peel the roasted tomatoes, then blend them into a puree.
4. Combine the tomato puree and Parmesan into the polenta; season with salt and pepper.

TENDER GREEK YOGURT PANCAKES WITH HONEY DRIZZLE

TOTAL TIME: 20 minutes	CALORIES: 422	SERVINGS: 1	CARBS: 70g	PROTEIN: 22g	FATS: 6g

INGREDIENTS:

- 1/2 cup all-purpose flour
- 1/4 cup Greek yogurt
- 1 large egg
- 1 tablespoon honey
- 1/2 teaspoon baking powder
- 1/4 cup whole milk
- Salt to taste

INSTRUCTIONS:

1. In a mixing bowl, combine flour, Greek yogurt, whole milk, and egg; add baking powder and a pinch of salt; whisk until smooth.
2. Heat a non-stick pan over low heat to avoid crust formation.
3. Pour batter into the pan for smaller pancakes; cook on very low heat for approximately 6 minutes and cover to steam-cook, preventing browning.

CREAMED SPINACH AND RICOTTA EGG BAKE

TOTAL TIME: 30 minutes	CALORIES: 310	SERVINGS: 1	CARBS: 6g	PROTEIN: 18g	FATS: 24g

INGREDIENTS:

- 1 cup fresh spinach
- 1/4 cup ricotta cheese
- 1 large egg
- 1 tablespoon olive oil
- Salt and pepper to taste

INSTRUCTIONS:

1. Preheat your oven to 350°F.
2. Heat olive oil in a pan over medium heat; add spinach and cook for 4 minutes; season with salt and pepper; blend until smooth.
3. In a small bowl, mix the spinach puree with ricotta cheese.
4. Transfer the spinach and ricotta mixture to a small baking dish; make a well in the center and crack the egg into it.
5. Bake in the preheated oven for 15 minutes; ensure there is no formed crust or firm parts by covering the baking dish with foil while baking.

TOFU AND VEGETABLE SCRAMBLE

TOTAL TIME: 20 minutes	CALORIES: 504	SERVINGS: 1	CARBS: 25g	PROTEIN: 21g	FATS: 38g

INGREDIENTS:

- 200g firm tofu
- 1 small bell pepper
- 1 small zucchini
- 1 medium carrot
- 1 small onion
- 2 cloves garlic
- 2 tablespoons olive oil
- 1/2 teaspoon turmeric
- Salt and pepper to taste

INSTRUCTIONS:

1. Finely chop bell pepper, zucchini, and onion; peel and grate the carrot; mince the garlic.
2. Drain the tofu and crumble it into small, bite-sized pieces.
3. In a large skillet, heat olive oil over medium heat; add onion and garlic; sauté for 5 minutes; add the crumbled tofu to the skillet; stir in turmeric, salt, and pepper; cook for 5 minutes, stirring frequently.
4. Add the chopped bell pepper, zucchini, and grated carrot to the skillet. Cook for an additional 7 minutes.

STEAMED COD WITH LEEK PURÉE AND COUSCOUS PILAF

TOTAL TIME: 30 minutes	CALORIES: 490	SERVINGS: 1	CARBS: 50g	PROTEIN: 37g	FATS: 16g

INGREDIENTS:

- 150g cod filet
- 1 cup leeks
- 1/2 cup couscous
- 1 tablespoon olive oil
- 1 cup vegetable broth
- Salt and pepper to taste
- 1/2 teaspoon lemon juice

INSTRUCTIONS:

1. Heat olive oil in a saucepan over medium heat; sauté chopped leeks for 7 minutes; add 1/2 cup broth, simmer for 5 minutes; blend to smooth purée; season with salt and pepper.
2. Bring remaining 1/2 cup broth to a boil; add couscous, cover, remove from heat, let stand for 5 minutes; fluff and mash for soft texture.
3. Season cod with salt, pepper, and lemon juice; steam in basket over boiling water for 8 minutes until flaky.
4. Place couscous on plate; top with steamed cod; cover with leek purée.

MILLET DUMPLINGS IN CREAMY MUSHROOM SAUCE

TOTAL TIME: 30 minutes	CALORIES: 1182	SERVINGS: 1	CARBS: 53g	PROTEIN: 13g	FATS: 104g

INGREDIENTS:

- 1/2 cup millet flour
- 1/4 cup water
- 1/2 teaspoon salt
- 1 cup portobello mushrooms
- 1 tablespoon olive oil
- 1 cup heavy cream
- Salt and pepper to taste

INSTRUCTIONS:

1. Combine millet flour, water, and 1/2 teaspoon salt to form a soft dough; shape into small, bite-sized dumplings; steam over boiling water for 10 minutes.
2. Heat olive oil in a pan; add mushrooms and sauté for 5 minutes; add heavy cream, simmer for 5 minutes; season with salt and pepper.
3. Add steamed dumplings to the creamy mushroom sauce; gently mix to coat the dumplings.

CHICKPEA SPINACH CURRY

TOTAL TIME: 20 minutes	CALORIES: 915	SERVINGS: 1	CARBS: 55g	PROTEIN: 18g	FATS: 74g

INGREDIENTS:

- 1 cup canned chickpeas
- 1 cup fresh spinach
- 1/2 cup coconut milk
- 1/4 cup onion
- 2 cloves garlic
- 1 tablespoon olive oil
- 1 teaspoon curry powder
- 1/2 teaspoon turmeric
- 1/2 teaspoon cumin
- Salt and pepper to taste

INSTRUCTIONS:

1. Heat olive oil in a pan over medium heat; sauté finely chopped onion and garlic for 4 minutes; add curry powder, turmeric, and cumin; cook for 1 minute; incorporate chickpeas and spinach; cook for 3 minutes; puree the ingredients.
2. Pour in coconut milk; simmer for 7 minutes, stirring occasionally; for a softer texture, add water to reach desired consistency.

PARMESAN CREAMY MUSHROOM RISOTTO

TOTAL TIME: 30 minutes	CALORIES: 450	SERVINGS: 1	CARBS: 58g	PROTEIN: 12g	FATS: 18g

INGREDIENTS:

- 1/2 cup Arborio rice
- 1 cup Shiitake mushrooms
- 2 cups chicken or vegetable broth
- 1/4 cup finely grated Parmesan cheese
- 1 tablespoon olive oil
- 1 small onion
- 1 clove garlic
- Salt and pepper to taste

INSTRUCTIONS:

1. Heat olive oil in a pan over medium heat; sauté finely chopped onion and garlic for 4 minutes; add mushrooms (stem removed); cook until they are soft and their moisture has been released, about 7 minutes.
2. Stir in Arborio rice; cook for 2 minutes to lightly toast the rice grains.
3. Gradually add broth, a half cup at a time, stirring constantly; wait until each addition is almost fully absorbed before adding the next; continue for 20 minutes.
4. Stir in Parmesan cheese until melted and mixed through; season with salt and pepper.

POACHED SCALLOPS ON SAFFRON CAULIFLOWER MASH

TOTAL TIME: 20 minutes	CALORIES: 599	SERVINGS: 1	CARBS: 8g	PROTEIN: 29g	FATS: 50g

INGREDIENTS:

- 5 large scallops
- 1 cup cauliflower florets
- 1 pinch saffron threads
- 2 tablespoons olive oil
- 1/4 cup heavy cream
- 1/2 cup chicken or vegetable broth
- Salt and pepper to taste
- 1 teaspoon lemon juice

INSTRUCTIONS:

1. Place cauliflower florets in a steaming basket over boiling water; steam for 8 minutes; transfer to a blender, add heavy cream, saffron threads dissolved in 1 tablespoon hot water, olive oil, and season with salt and pepper; blend until smooth.
2. In a small skillet, bring chicken broth and lemon juice to a gentle simmer; add scallops and poach gently until opaque and tender, about 2-3 minutes per side.
3. Spoon saffron cauliflower mash onto a plate; top with poached scallops; drizzle a little of the poaching liquid over the scallops for added flavor.

SPINACH ARTICHOKE MAC AND CHEESE CUPS

TOTAL TIME: 30 minutes	CALORIES: 450	SERVINGS: 1	CARBS: 35g	PROTEIN: 15g	FATS: 27g

INGREDIENTS:

- 1/2 cup elbow macaroni
- 1/4 cup cream cheese
- 1/4 cup shredded mozzarella cheese
- 1/4 cup chopped canned artichoke hearts
- 1/2 cup fresh spinach
- 2 tablespoons whole milk
- 1 tablespoon unsalted butter
- Salt and pepper to taste
- 1/4 teaspoon garlic powder

INSTRUCTIONS:

1. Boil macaroni for 17 minutes; drain.
2. In a saucepan, melt butter; add cream cheese, mozzarella, and milk; stir until smooth and creamy.
3. Stir in pureed spinach and artichoke hearts; season with garlic powder, salt, and pepper.
4. Combine the cheese sauce with the soft-cooked macaroni; mix thoroughly.
5. Ensure the mixture is smooth and homogeneous; if needed, pulse in a food processor to achieve a soft, uniform consistency.

GROUND TURKEY WITH BUTTERNUT SQUASH AND SAGE MASH

TOTAL TIME: 30 minutes	CALORIES: 646	SERVINGS: 1	CARBS: 23g	PROTEIN: 51g	FATS: 42g

INGREDIENTS:

- 200g ground turkey
- 1 cup butternut squash
- 1 tablespoon olive oil
- 1/4 teaspoon ground sage
- Salt and pepper to taste
- 1/4 cup chicken broth or milk
- 1 tablespoon butter

INSTRUCTIONS:

1. Place cubed butternut squash in a microwave-safe bowl with a splash of water; cover and microwave on high for 10 minutes.
2. Heat olive oil in a skillet over medium heat; add ground turkey, season with salt, pepper, and ground sage; cook for 10 minutes.
3. Once squash is tender, drain any excess water, add chicken broth or milk and butter; mash thoroughly or blend until completely smooth with no lumps.
4. Mix the soft cooked turkey into the butternut squash purée, ensuring the mixture is cohesive and uniform.

CHICKEN OVER SOFT POLENTA WITH OLIVES AND CAPERS

TOTAL TIME: 30 minutes	CALORIES: 704	SERVINGS: 1	CARBS: 41g	PROTEIN: 36g	FATS: 46g

INGREDIENTS:

- 200g ground chicken
- 1/2 cup instant polenta
- 2 cups chicken broth
- 1 tablespoon capers
- 1/4 cup olives
- 1 tablespoon olive oil
- 1 clove garlic
- 1/4 cup milk
- 1 tablespoon unsalted butter
- Salt and pepper to taste

INSTRUCTIONS:

1. Bring 1.5 cups of chicken broth to a boil; gradually whisk in polenta; reduce heat and stir continuously for 5 minutes; stir in milk and butter until smooth; season with salt.
2. In a skillet, heat olive oil over medium heat; add ground chicken, breaking it apart as it cooks; cook for 7 minutes.
3. Stir in pureed capers, olives and garlic; add remaining 1/2 cup chicken broth; simmer gently for 5 minutes.
4. Adjust seasoning with salt and pepper; ensure the chicken mixture is fully cooked and cohesive.

STEAMED SEA BASS OVER MAQUE CHOUX

TOTAL TIME: 30 minutes	CALORIES: 721	SERVINGS: 1	CARBS: 55g	PROTEIN: 54g	FATS: 36g

INGREDIENTS:

- 1 sea bass filet
- 1 cup fresh corn kernels
- 1/2 red bell pepper
- 1/2 green bell pepper
- 1/4 cup onion
- 1 clove garlic
- 1 tablespoon olive oil
- 1/2 cup vegetable broth
- 1 tablespoon heavy cream
- Salt and pepper to taste

INSTRUCTIONS:

1. Season the sea bass filet with salt and pepper; place in a steamer over boiling water; steam for 8 minutes.
2. In a skillet, heat olive oil over medium heat; add pureed onion, garlic, corn and bell peppers; cook for 7 minutes. Add vegetable broth and cream; simmer gently for an additional 7 minutes.
3. Spoon the Maque Choux onto a plate; place the steamed sea bass on top.

SPINACH AND FETA POLENTA CAKES WITH EGGPLANT RAGOUT

TOTAL TIME: 30 minutes	CALORIES: 582	SERVINGS: 1	CARBS: 55g	PROTEIN: 12g	FATS: 38g

INGREDIENTS:

- 1/2 cup instant polenta
- 2 cups water
- 1/4 cup feta cheese
- 1 cup spinach
- 1 tablespoon olive oil
- 1 small eggplant
- 1/2 cup tomato sauce
- 1 clove garlic
- 1/4 cup onions
- 1 tablespoon olive oil
- Salt and pepper to taste

INSTRUCTIONS:

1. Boil 2 cups of water in a saucepan; slowly whisk in instant polenta and reduce heat, stirring continuously for 5 minutes; mix in the pureed spinach and blended feta until smooth; season with salt and pepper.
2. Lightly oil ramekins or a muffin tin; spoon the polenta mixture into it.
3. Heat 1 tablespoon of olive oil in a skillet; sauté the chopped onions and garlic for 3 minutes; add the finely diced and peeled eggplant and cook for 10 minutes; stir in the smooth tomato sauce and simmer for 5 minutes.
4. Spoon a generous amount of the eggplant ragout over each polenta cake directly in the ramekin or muffin cup.

SALMON AND GOAT CHEESE FRITTATA WITH CAPERS

TOTAL TIME: 30 minutes	CALORIES: 655	SERVINGS: 1	CARBS: 3g	PROTEIN: 45g	FATS: 51g

INGREDIENTS:

- 1 salmon filet
- 3 large eggs
- 1/4 cup goat cheese
- 1 tablespoon capers
- 1/4 cup whole milk
- 2 tablespoons olive oil
- Salt and pepper to taste

INSTRUCTIONS:

1. Poach the salmon in simmering water for 8 minutes; flake the salmon into small pieces.
2. In a bowl, whisk together eggs, whole milk, salt, and pepper until smooth; stir in mashed goat cheese and capers.
3. Heat olive oil in a non-stick skillet over medium-low heat; pour in the egg mixture; scatter the flaked salmon evenly; cook for 7 minutes.
4. Cover the skillet with a lid to let the top of the frittata set, ensuring it remains soft and moist, about 3 more minutes. Avoid browning or crisping.

POACHED TROUT WITH LEMON BUTTER AND HERBED POTATOES

TOTAL TIME: 30 minutes	CALORIES: 510	SERVINGS: 1	CARBS: 15g	PROTEIN: 25g	FATS: 39g

INGREDIENTS:

- 1 trout filet
- 1 tablespoon unsalted butter
- 1 teaspoon lemon juice
- 1 medium potato
- 1 tablespoon heavy cream
- 1 tablespoon olive oil
- Salt and pepper to taste

INSTRUCTIONS:

1. Place trout filet in a shallow pan; cover with water; add a pinch of salt and a splash of lemon juice; bring to a gentle simmer, cover, and poach for 8 minutes.
2. Boil the chopped and peeled potato until very soft; drain and mash with heavy cream and olive oil until smooth; season with salt and pepper to taste.
3. In a small saucepan, melt butter over low heat and mix in lemon juice.
4. Place the poached trout on a plate, drizzle with lemon butter sauce, and serve alongside the mashed potatoes.

CANNED TUNA AVOCADO QUINOA BOWL

TOTAL TIME: 30 minutes	CALORIES: 820	SERVINGS: 1	CARBS: 42g	PROTEIN: 34g	FATS: 58g

INGREDIENTS:

- 1 cup cooked quinoa
- 1 can of tuna
- 1 ripe avocado
- 2 tablespoons olive oil
- 1 tablespoon lemon juice
- 2 tablespoons mayonnaise
- Salt and pepper to taste

INSTRUCTIONS:

1. Cook quinoa in a ratio of 2:1 water to quinoa; bring to a boil and simmer for 20 minutes; mash lightly if necessary to ensure no hard grains remain.
2. Drain and mash the canned tuna.
3. In a bowl, combine the mashed avocado, mashed tuna, and quinoa; mix thoroughly to ensure all elements are well incorporated.
4. Stir in olive oil, lemon juice, and mayonnaise; mix thoroughly.

TERIYAKI TURKEY MEATBALLS

TOTAL TIME: 30 minutes	CALORIES: 510	SERVINGS: 1	CARBS: 22g	PROTEIN: 35g	FATS: 27g

INGREDIENTS:

- 200g ground turkey
- 1 slice of whole wheat bread
- 1 egg
- 2 tablespoons teriyaki sauce
- 1 tablespoon soy sauce
- 1 tablespoon honey
- 1/2 teaspoon garlic powder
- 1/2 teaspoon ginger powder
- 2 tablespoons vegetable oil
- 1/2 cup chicken broth
- Milk

INSTRUCTIONS:

1. Remove crusts from bread; use a food processor to process the bread until the crumbs are uniform; moisten these breadcrumbs with milk until soft.
2. In a large bowl, combine the finely ground turkey, moistened breadcrumbs, beaten egg, salt, and pepper.
3. Shape the mixture into bite-sized balls; heat vegetable oil in a skillet over medium heat; gently brown meatballs on all sides, approximately 5 minutes, taking care not to create a crust.
4. In a separate bowl, combine smooth and thick teriyaki sauce, soy sauce, honey, garlic powder, and ginger powder.
5. Add the teriyaki mixture and chicken broth to the skillet with the meatballs; reduce heat to low, cover, and let simmer for 18 minutes.

CREAMY POACHED CRAB SALAD

TOTAL TIME: 30 minutes	CALORIES: 657	SERVINGS: 1	CARBS: 8g	PROTEIN: 22g	FATS: 60g

INGREDIENTS:

- 200g crab meat
- 1/4 cup mayonnaise
- 1 tablespoon sour cream
- 1 teaspoon lemon juice
- 1/2 teaspoon Dijon mustard
- 5 leaves Bibb lettuce
- 1/4 avocado
- Salt and pepper to taste

INSTRUCTIONS:

1. If using fresh, poach in simmering water for 7 minutes; if using canned, ensure it's finely shredded or pureed.
2. In a bowl, combine mayonnaise, sour cream, lemon juice, and Dijon mustard until smooth.
3. Add prepared crab meat to the dressing; mix thoroughly to ensure the mixture is cohesive; season with salt and pepper.
4. Place chopped Bibb lettuce and avocado in a blender; add lemon juice, salt, and pepper.
5. Spoon the pureed lettuce base onto the plate first, forming a small bed; spoon the crab salad over the pureed lettuce.

SLOW-COOKED COCONUT SALMON CURRY

TOTAL TIME: 30 minutes	CALORIES: 510	SERVINGS: 1	CARBS: 8g	PROTEIN: 25g	FATS: 42g

INGREDIENTS:

- 1 salmon filet
- 1/2 cup coconut milk
- 1/2 cup vegetable broth
- 1 tablespoon curry powder
- 1 teaspoon turmeric
- 1/2 teaspoon ginger
- 1 garlic clove
- 1 tablespoon olive oil
- Salt and pepper to taste

INSTRUCTIONS:

1. Poach salmon in a mixture of vegetable broth and water for 10 minutes; remove from heat, flake finely with a fork, ensuring there are no large pieces.
2. In a skillet, heat olive oil over medium heat; add minced garlic and ginger; cook for 2 minutes; stir in curry powder and turmeric.
3. Add coconut milk to the skillet; bring to a gentle simmer; add the flaked salmon back into the skillet; stir.
4. Let the mixture simmer gently for an additional 5 minutes to allow flavors to meld.

SLOW-COOKED BEEF IN MUSHROOM STROGANOFF SAUCE

TOTAL TIME: 30 minutes	CALORIES: 711	SERVINGS: 1	CARBS: 19g	PROTEIN: 26g	FATS: 60g

INGREDIENTS:

- 150g finely ground beef
- 1/2 cup button mushrooms
- 1/4 cup onions
- 1 clove garlic
- 1 tablespoon all-purpose flour
- 1 cup beef broth
- 1/4 cup sour cream
- 1 tablespoon butter
- 1 teaspoon Worcestershire sauce
- Salt and pepper to taste
- 1 tablespoon olive oil

INSTRUCTIONS:

1. In a skillet, heat olive oil over medium heat; add chopped onions and garlic; cook for 3 minutes.
2. Introduce finely chopped mushrooms; cook for 5 minutes.
3. Stir in flour; cook for 2 minutes; gradually add beef broth, stirring continuously.
4. Add finely ground beef to the skillet; cook over medium heat, stirring frequently, for 7 minutes.
5. Add Worcestershire sauce, salt, and pepper; simmer gently for 2 minutes to blend the flavors; remove from heat and stir in sour cream.

GNOCCHI WITH SAGE-THYME BUTTERNUT SQUASH SAUCE

TOTAL TIME: 30 minutes	CALORIES: 651	SERVINGS: 1	CARBS: 79g	PROTEIN: 17g	FATS: 31g

INGREDIENTS:

- 200g pre-made potato gnocchi
- 1 cup butternut squash
- 2 tablespoons heavy cream
- 1 tablespoon butter
- 1 teaspoon dried sage
- 1/2 teaspoon dried thyme
- 1/4 cup vegetable broth
- Salt and pepper to taste
- Grated Parmesan cheese

INSTRUCTIONS:

1. Boil gnocchi in salted water according to package instructions until they float to the surface; drain and set aside.
2. In a saucepan, heat butter over medium heat; add cubed butternut squash, heavy cream, sage, thyme, salt, and pepper; stir to combine.
3. Add vegetable broth to the saucepan and stir until the sauce is smooth and creamy; adjust seasoning as needed.
4. Add cooked gnocchi to the sauce, gently stir to coat the gnocchi evenly with the sauce; let the gnocchi simmer in the sauce for a few minutes to absorb the flavors; sprinkle with finely grated Parmesan cheese.

CHICKEN AND VEGETABLE CASSEROLE

TOTAL TIME: 30 minutes	CALORIES: 923	SERVINGS: 1	CARBS: 28g	PROTEIN: 51g	FATS: 68g

INGREDIENTS:

- 150g ground chicken
- 1/2 cup carrots
- 1/2 cup celery
- 1/4 cup onion
- 2 cloves garlic
- 1/2 cup peas
- 1 cup chicken broth
- 1/2 cup cream
- 2 tablespoons olive oil
- 1 teaspoon thyme
- Salt and pepper to taste

INSTRUCTIONS:

1. Boil or steam the grated carrots for 7 minutes, then drain.
2. In a large skillet, heat olive oil over medium heat; add pureed peas, celery, onion and garlic; cook for 3 minutes.
3. Add the ground chicken to the skillet; cook while stirring for 10 minutes; add the carrots.
4. Sprinkle in thyme, salt, and pepper; pour in chicken broth and cream; mix well.
5. Let the casserole simmer gently for about 7 minutes.

GARLIC-STEAMED TOFU AND VEGETABLE RICE BOWL

TOTAL TIME: 30 minutes	CALORIES: 475	SERVINGS: 1	CARBS: 56g	PROTEIN: 13g	FATS: 23g

INGREDIENTS:

- 1/2 cup silken tofu
- 1/3 cup grated carrots
- 1/3 cup grated zucchini
- 3/4 cup white rice
- 2 tablespoons soy sauce
- 1 teaspoon minced garlic
- 2 teaspoons sesame oil
- 1/2 avocado
- 1.5 cups water
- Salt

INSTRUCTIONS:

1. Combine rice with water and a pinch of salt in a pot; bring to a boil, then simmer covered for 20 minutes; keep covered off the heat for 5 more minutes.
2. Finely grate the carrots and peele the zucchini; mince garlic; mash avocado.
3. Place silken tofu and grated vegetables in a steaming basket; steam over boiling water for 15 minutes.
4. Mix soy sauce, sesame oil, and minced garlic in a small bowl.
5. Mix steamed tofu and vegetables with sauce; add the mashed avocado and mix gently; serve over soft, slightly overcooked rice.

QUINOA AND BLACK BEAN STUFFED BELL PEPPERS

TOTAL TIME: 30 minutes	CALORIES: 914	SERVINGS: 1	CARBS: 90g	PROTEIN: 39g	FATS: 47g

INGREDIENTS:

- 2 large bell peppers
- 1/2 cup quinoa
- 1 cup canned black beans
- 2 cups spinach
- 4 tablespoons tomato sauce
- 2 tablespoons olive oil
- 1/2 teaspoon ground cumin
- Salt to taste
- 1/2 cup ricotta or cream cheese

INSTRUCTIONS:

1. Add the quinoa to a pot with water; bring to a boil; reduce heat, simmer for 15 minutes until fluffy.
2. Halve and peel the peppers, remove seeds; microwave for 5 minutes.
3. Combine the cooked quinoa, mashed black beans, pureed spinach, tomato sauce, olive oil, cumin, and salt; ensure the mixture is smooth.
4. Fill each pepper half with the quinoa mixture; place the stuffed peppers in a baking dish, cover with foil; bake at 350°F for 15 minutes.
5. Top with ricotta or cream cheese post-baking.

CREAMY SOFT VEGETABLE KORMA

TOTAL TIME: 30 minutes	CALORIES: 570	SERVINGS: 1	CARBS: 24g	PROTEIN: 8g	FATS: 50g

INGREDIENTS:

- 2/3 cup cauliflower
- 1/2 cup carrots
- 1/2 cup peas
- 1/3 cup coconut milk
- 1 tablespoon olive oil
- 3/4 teaspoon ground turmeric
- 3/4 teaspoon garam masala
- 1/2 teaspoon ground cumin
- 1/4 teaspoon ground coriander
- Salt to taste
- 1/4 cup heavy cream

INSTRUCTIONS:

1. Boil cauliflower, carrots, and peas for 12 minutes; mash or puree vegetables thoroughly to ensure no lumps remain.
2. Heat olive oil in a pan; add turmeric, garam masala, cumin, coriander, and salt; stir in coconut milk and bring to a gentle simmer.
3. Add mashed vegetables to the sauce; mix well to ensure a smooth consistency; adjust the thickness with a little water if necessary.
4. Stir in heavy cream and heat through just until hot, ensuring not to boil.

EGGPLANT AND TOMATO BASIL RELISH WITH SOFT ZUCCHINI

TOTAL TIME: 20 minutes	CALORIES: 207	SERVINGS: 1	CARBS: 20g	PROTEIN: 3g	FATS: 14g

INGREDIENTS:

- 1/2 medium eggplant
- 1 medium tomato
- 1/4 cup fresh basil leaves
- 1/2 medium zucchini
- 1 tablespoon olive oil
- Salt and pepper to taste

INSTRUCTIONS:

1. Pierce eggplant with a fork; microwave on high for 7 minutes; cool slightly.
2. Slice zucchini and steam in a microwave-safe dish with a bit of water, covered, for 5 minutes.
3. Microwave tomatoes for 4 minutes; blend tomatoes and fresh basil leaves in a blender until smooth.
4. Scoop out the inside of the softened eggplant and blend with the tomato-basil mixture; add olive oil, salt, and pepper; blend until smooth.
5. Serve the eggplant and tomato basil relish over the steamed zucchini slices.

LEMON AND DILL MASHED POTATOES WITH YOGURT

TOTAL TIME: 15 minutes	CALORIES: 441	SERVINGS: 1	CARBS: 66g	PROTEIN: 13g	FATS: 15g

INGREDIENTS:

- 1 large potato
- 1/4 cup plain Greek yogurt
- 1 tablespoon olive oil
- 1 tablespoon fresh dill
- 1/2 lemon
- Salt and pepper to taste

INSTRUCTIONS:

1. Peel the potato and cut into small cubes; place in a microwave-safe bowl with a splash of water; cover with a lid or plastic wrap; microwave on high for 12 minutes.
2. Drain any excess water from the potatoes; add Greek yogurt, olive oil, lemon juice, and dill to the potatoes; mash until smooth and well combined; season with salt and pepper to taste.

GARLIC BUTTER WHITE BEAN MASH WITH SOFT CARROT

TOTAL TIME: 20 minutes	CALORIES: 796	SERVINGS: 1	CARBS: 67g	PROTEIN: 20g	FATS: 51g

INGREDIENTS:

- 1 cup canned white beans
- 2 large carrots
- 2 tablespoons butter
- 1 clove garlic
- Salt and pepper to taste
- 2 tablespoons olive oil

INSTRUCTIONS:

1. Slice the carrots into thin strips; steam the carrot strips for 10 minutes.
2. In a pan, melt butter over medium heat; add minced garlic and cook for 2 minutes; add white beans, salt, and pepper; mash the mixture until smooth, or blend in a food processor for a finer texture; stir in olive oil to enrich the dip and ensure a smooth, creamy texture.
3. Arrange the steamed carrot strips on a plate; place the garlic butter white bean mash in a bowl for dipping.

CREAMY FETA AND OLIVE SPREAD WITH SOFT BREAD

TOTAL TIME: 20 minutes	CALORIES: 644	SERVINGS: 1	CARBS: 20g	PROTEIN: 17g	FATS: 56g

INGREDIENTS:

- 1/2 cup feta cheese
- 1/4 cup pitted Kalamata olives
- 1/4 cup cream cheese
- 1 tablespoon olive oil
- 1 clove garlic
- 1 slice of soft whole wheat bread
- Milk or vegetable stock
- Salt and pepper to taste

INSTRUCTIONS:

1. Place feta cheese, Kalamata olives, cream cheese, olive oil, salt, pepper and minced garlic in a food processor.
2. Pulse bread in a food processor to fine crumbs (<0.1in); in a square mould on a plate, add half the breadcrumbs; moisten with milk or stock; fill mould with the spread, top with remaining breadcrumbs, and moisten again; cover and refrigerate for 1 hour to set.
3. Remove from mould and cut into bite-sized pieces.

RICOTTA AND ROASTED RED PEPPER PUREE WITH SOFT BREAD

TOTAL TIME: 30 minutes	CALORIES: 406	SERVINGS: 1	CARBS: 25g	PROTEIN: 15g	FATS: 29g

INGREDIENTS:

- 1 large red bell pepper
- 1/2 cup ricotta cheese
- 1 tablespoon olive oil
- Salt and pepper to taste
- 1 slice of soft whole wheat bread
- Milk or vegetable stock

INSTRUCTIONS:

1. Set the oven to broil at 450°F; place the pepper on a foil-lined baking sheet; broil, turning occasionally, until all sides are blackened, about 15 minutes.
2. Place in a bowl, cover with plastic wrap for 10 minutes, then peel under cool water, remove seeds and membranes.
3. Trim crusts from bread; pulse bread in a food processor to fine crumbs (<0.1in); in a square mould on a plate, add half the breadcrumbs. Moisten with milk or vegetable stock.
4. Combine roasted pepper, ricotta, olive oil, salt, and pepper in a blender; blend until smooth.
5. Spread ricotta-pepper mixture over bread base; top with remaining breadcrumbs, and moisten again.
6. Cover and refrigerate for 1 hour to set; remove from mould and cut into bite-sized pieces.

GREEK YOGURT AND HONEY WITH PUREED FIG

TOTAL TIME: 5 minutes	CALORIES: 463	SERVINGS: 1	CARBS: 91g	PROTEIN: 27g	FATS: 5g

INGREDIENTS:

- 1 cup Greek yogurt
- 2 tablespoons honey
- 5 fresh figs
- A pinch of ground cinnamon

INSTRUCTIONS:

1. Place figs in a blender.
2. In a bowl, combine Greek yogurt and honey; stir thoroughly until the honey is well incorporated into the yogurt.
3. Mix the fig puree with the yogurt and honey mixture; stir in optional cinnamon if desired.

OLIVE OIL AND GARLIC MASHED CAULIFLOWER

TOTAL TIME: 20 minutes	CALORIES: 196	SERVINGS: 1	CARBS: 16g	PROTEIN: 6g	FATS: 14g

INGREDIENTS:

- 1/2 medium cauliflower
- 1 tablespoon olive oil
- 1 clove garlic
- Salt and pepper to taste

INSTRUCTIONS:

1. Chop the cauliflower into small florets; place florets in a microwave-safe dish with a splash of water, cover with a lid or plastic wrap, and microwave on high for 10 minutes.
2. Drain any excess water from the cauliflower; while still hot, add olive oil and minced garlic to the cauliflower; use a hand blender or potato masher to mash the cauliflower until smooth and creamy; season with salt and pepper to taste.

CREAMY TOMATO BASIL SOUP

TOTAL TIME: 20 minutes	CALORIES: 537	SERVINGS: 1	CARBS: 22g	PROTEIN: 6g	FATS: 50g

INGREDIENTS:

- 4 medium tomatoes
- 1/4 cup heavy cream
- 2 tablespoons olive oil
- 1/4 cup fresh basil
- 1 clove garlic
- Salt and pepper to taste

INSTRUCTIONS:

1. In a medium saucepan, heat olive oil over medium heat; add minced garlic and cook until fragrant, about 1 minute; add peeled and chopped tomatoes and cook for 7 minutes.
2. Transfer the tomato mixture to a blender; add chopped basil; blend until completely smooth.
3. Return the blended soup to the saucepan; stir in heavy cream; heat over low heat just until hot, do not boil; season with salt and pepper.

CREAMY BAKED RICOTTA WITH LEMON ZEST AND BUTTERNUT SQUASH

TOTAL TIME: 15 minutes	CALORIES: 420	SERVINGS: 1	CARBS: 25g	PROTEIN: 16g	FATS: 36g

INGREDIENTS:

- 1/2 cup ricotta cheese
- 1/4 teaspoon lemon zest
- 1 tablespoon olive oil
- 2 tablespoons of cream
- 1 cup butternut squash
- Salt and pepper to taste

INSTRUCTIONS:

1. Place the peeled and chopped butternut squash in a steamer or microwave-safe dish with a splash of water; cover and steam for 8 minutes.
2. In a bowl, combine ricotta cheese, lemon zest, salt, pepper and olive oil; mix until smooth.
3. Transfer the ricotta mixture to a small saucepan; add cream; warm the ricotta over very low heat for 5 minutes, stirring constantly to prevent it from sticking to the pan or forming a crust.
4. Once steamed, blend the butternut squash until smooth using a food processor or blender.
5. Spoon the ricotta onto a plate and top with the butternut squash puree.

SMOOTH LENTIL SOUP

TOTAL TIME: 20 minutes	CALORIES: 393	SERVINGS: 1	CARBS: 49g	PROTEIN: 19g	FATS: 15g

INGREDIENTS:

- 1 cup canned lentils
- 2 cups vegetable broth
- 1/4 cup chopped onion
- 1 clove garlic
- 1 tablespoon olive oil
- 1/2 teaspoon ground cumin
- Salt and pepper to taste

INSTRUCTIONS:

1. Heat olive oil in a saucepan over medium heat; add minced garlic and chopped onion; sauté for 2 minutes.
2. Add rinsed and drained lentils, vegetable broth, and ground cumin to the saucepan; bring to a simmer and cook for 13 minutes.
3. Transfer the soup to a blender; blend until completely smooth, ensuring there are no lumps or pieces; serve hot.

SMOOTH ARTICHOKE HEART AND BASIL DIP WITH SOFT BREAD

TOTAL TIME: 20 minutes	CALORIES: 308	SERVINGS: 1	CARBS: 35g	PROTEIN: 12g	FATS: 16g

INGREDIENTS:

- 200g artichoke hearts
- 2 tablespoons fresh basil leaves
- 1 tablespoon olive oil
- 1/2 clove garlic
- 1 tablespoon grated Parmesan cheese
- 1/2 slice of soft whole wheat bread
- A splash of milk
- Salt and pepper to taste

INSTRUCTIONS:

1. Drain and combine artichoke hearts, fresh basil, olive oil, minced garlic, salt, pepper and Parmesan cheese in a food processor; blend until the mixture is completely smooth.
2. Pulse bread in a food processor to fine crumbs (<0.1in); in a square mould on a plate, add half the breadcrumbs; moisten with milk; fill mould with the mixture, top with remaining breadcrumbs, and moisten again; cover and refrigerate for 1 hour to set.
3. Remove from mould and cut into bite-sized pieces.

LEMON CHICKPEA AND TAHINI DIP WITH SOFT BREAD

TOTAL TIME: 20 minutes	CALORIES: 424	SERVINGS: 1	CARBS: 41g	PROTEIN: 14g	FATS: 25g

INGREDIENTS:

- 100g canned chickpeas
- 1 tablespoon tahini
- Juice of 1/2 lemon
- 1/2 clove garlic
- 1 tablespoon olive oil
- 1/2 slice of soft whole wheat bread
- A splash of milk

INSTRUCTIONS:

1. Place rinsed and drained chickpeas, tahini, lemon juice, minced garlic, salt and olive oil in a blender or food processor; blend until the mixture is completely smooth.
2. Pulse bread in a food processor to fine crumbs (<0.1in); in a square mould on a plate, add half the breadcrumbs; moisten with milk; fill mould with the mixture, top with remaining breadcrumbs, and moisten again; cover and refrigerate for 1 hour to set.
3. Remove from mould and cut into bite-sized pieces.

BANOFFEE PIE PUDDING

TOTAL TIME: 20 minutes	CALORIES: 617	SERVINGS: 1	CARBS: 102g	PROTEIN: 8g	FATS: 17g

INGREDIENTS:

- 1/2 cup banana
- 1/4 cup dulce de leche or caramel sauce
- 1/2 cup whipped cream
- 1/4 cup ready-made vanilla pudding mix

INSTRUCTIONS:

1. Prepare the pudding mix according to package instructions to ensure a smooth texture.
2. Mash the banana until very smooth.
3. In a serving bowl, layer the mashed banana at the bottom; spread a layer of dulce de leche or caramel sauce over the banana; add a layer of vanilla pudding over the caramel; spread whipped cream over the top of the pudding layer.
4. Refrigerate for 10 minutes before serving.

CHOCOLATE MOUSSE

TOTAL TIME: 15 minutes	CALORIES: 759	SERVINGS: 1	CARBS: 33g	PROTEIN: 4g	FATS: 64g

INGREDIENTS:

- 1/2 cup heavy cream
- 2 ounces high-quality dark chocolate
- 1 tablespoon sugar
- 1/2 teaspoon vanilla extract

INSTRUCTIONS:

1. Place the chopped chocolate in a heat-proof bowl and melt it using a microwave in short bursts of 20 seconds, stirring in between.
2. In a separate bowl, whip the heavy cream with sugar and vanilla extract until it forms soft peaks. Be careful not to overwhip.
3. Once the chocolate has melted and slightly cooled, fold it into the whipped cream until the mixture is uniform. Avoid vigorous stirring to maintain a light texture.
4. Spoon the mousse into a serving dish or a ramekin. Refrigerate for 15 minutes to set slightly before serving.

CINNAMON ROLLS PARFAIT

TOTAL TIME: 20 minutes	CALORIES: 546	SERVINGS: 1	CARBS: 81g	PROTEIN: 11g	FATS: 22g

INGREDIENTS:

- 1/2 cup vanilla yogurt
- 1 small cinnamon roll (ensure it's very soft; if not available, use soft whole wheat bread mixed with cinnamon and sugar, then moistened)
- 1/4 cup cream cheese
- 2 tablespoons maple syrup
- 1/4 teaspoon ground cinnamon

INSTRUCTIONS:

1. If using a cinnamon roll, ensure it is extremely soft; microwave for 20 seconds if needed to soften further; puree the cinnamon roll in a blender until completely smooth; if necessary, add a little milk to achieve a soft, spreadable consistency.
2. In a bowl, mix softened cream cheese with maple syrup and cinnamon.
3. In a serving glass or bowl, layer half of the cream cheese mixture; add a layer of the pureed cinnamon roll; top with vanilla yogurt; repeat the layers if the serving container allows, or according to preference.
4. Refrigerate for 10 minutes.

FRUIT TART PUREE

TOTAL TIME: 20 minutes	CALORIES: 285	SERVINGS: 1	CARBS: 69g	PROTEIN: 5g	FATS: 3g

INGREDIENTS:

- 1/2 cup ripe peaches
- 1/2 cup ripe mangoes
- 1/2 banana
- 1/2 cup strawberries
- 1/4 cup vanilla yogurt
- 1 tablespoon honey to sweeten if needed

INSTRUCTIONS:

1. Ensure the strawberries are hulled, peaches and mangoes peeled and sliced, banana peeled; briefly cook the peaches, mangoes, and strawberries in a small saucepan with a splash of water just until they are soft and start to break down, about 6 minutes. This step is optional but helps in softening the fruits further.
2. Place all cooked fruits and banana into a blender; add vanilla yogurt and honey; blend until completely smooth.
3. Refrigerate the puree for 15 minutes.

SOFT SPONGE MACARON CAKE

TOTAL TIME: 30 minutes	CALORIES: 979	SERVINGS: 1	CARBS: 81g	PROTEIN: 28g	FATS: 64

INGREDIENTS:

- 1/2 cup almond flour
- 1/4 cup sugar
- 2 large eggs
- 1/4 teaspoon almond extract
- 2 tablespoons butter
- 1/4 cup milk
- 1/4 cup prepared vanilla pudding or custard

INSTRUCTIONS:

1. Preheat the oven to 350°F.
2. Blend almond flour and sugar together in a mixing bowl; add eggs, almond extract, and melted butter; mix until smooth; gradually incorporate milk to maintain a smooth batter; pour batter into a greased or parchment-lined small baking dish; bake for 15 minutes, or until a toothpick comes out clean; allow cake to cool; remove from pan.
3. Puree cake in a food processor until fine; mix cake crumbs with vanilla pudding to create a soft, cohesive mixture.
4. Refrigerate for 10 minutes to set before serving.

PEACH AND MANGO STICKY RICE PUREE

TOTAL TIME: 30 minutes	CALORIES: 261	SERVINGS: 1	CARBS: 51g	PROTEIN: 3g	FATS: 7g

INGREDIENTS:

- 1/4 cup sticky rice
- 1/4 cup ripe mango
- 1/4 cup ripe peach
- 1/4 cup coconut milk
- 1 tablespoon honey
- A pinch of salt

INSTRUCTIONS:

1. Prepare sticky rice according to package instructions until it's soft and sticky; let it cool slightly.
2. In a blender, puree the peeled and chopped mango and peach until completely smooth.
3. Mix the fruit puree with the sticky rice in a bowl. Add coconut milk, honey, and a pinch of salt; blend the mixture again until completely smooth; if too thick, adjust by adding more coconut milk to achieve a smooth texture.
4. Serve immediately or chill in the refrigerator for 15 minutes.

VANILLA PANNA COTTA

TOTAL TIME: 15 minutes	CALORIES: 355	SERVINGS: 1	CARBS: 30g	PROTEIN: 6g	FATS: 24g

INGREDIENTS:

- 1/4 cup whole milk
- 1/2 cup heavy cream
- 1 1/2 teaspoons unflavored gelatin
- 2 tablespoons sugar
- 1/2 teaspoon vanilla extract

INSTRUCTIONS:

1. Sprinkle gelatin over 2 tablespoons of cold milk in a small bowl; let stand for 5 minutes to soften.
2. Combine remaining milk, heavy cream, and sugar in a saucepan; heat over medium until just simmering, stirring to dissolve sugar.
3. Add the gelatin mixture to the hot cream mixture; stir until gelatin is completely dissolved; remove from heat; stir in vanilla extract.
4. Pour mixture into a ramekin or mold; let cool to room temperature; refrigerate for 20 minutes to set.

RED VELVET CAKE MOUSSE

TOTAL TIME: 30 minutes	CALORIES: 685	SERVINGS: 1	CARBS: 37g	PROTEIN: 5g	FATS: 58g

INGREDIENTS:

- 1/4 cup prepared red velvet cake mix
- 1/2 cup heavy cream
- 2 tablespoons cream cheese
- 1 tablespoon sugar
- 1/2 teaspoon vanilla extract
- Red food coloring (optional)

INSTRUCTIONS:

1. Prepare a small amount of red velvet cake as per the box instructions, then puree it in a blender until completely smooth.
2. In a bowl, whip the heavy cream, sugar, and vanilla extract until soft peaks form.
3. In another bowl, blend the softened cream cheese until smooth, adding a drop of red food coloring if a more vibrant color is desired.
4. Fold the cream cheese and the pureed cake into the whipped cream to maintain a fluffy texture; spoon the mixture into a serving dish and refrigerate for at least 20 minutes to set.

LEMON PASSET

TOTAL TIME: 30 minutes	CALORIES: 630	SERVINGS: 1	CARBS: 57g	PROTEIN: 8g	FATS: 43g

INGREDIENTS:

- 1/2 cup heavy cream
- 1/4 cup sugar
- 2 tablespoons lemon juice
- 1 lemon zest
- 1 teaspoon gelatin powder
- 1/4 cup water

INSTRUCTIONS:

1. Sprinkle gelatin over the water in a small bowl; let it stand for 5 minutes to soften.
2. In a saucepan, combine lemon juice, half of the sugar, and lemon zest; warm over medium heat until the sugar dissolves; add the gelatin mixture to the saucepan and stir until fully dissolved; remove from heat.
3. In a separate bowl, whip the heavy cream with the remaining sugar until soft peaks form.
4. Fold the lemon mixture into the whipped cream until well combined; pour the mixture into a serving dish and refrigerate for 20 minutes.

STRAWBERRY SHORTCAKE PUDDING

TOTAL TIME: 15 minutes	CALORIES: 427	SERVINGS: 1	CARBS: 48g	PROTEIN: 1g	FATS: 26g

INGREDIENTS:

- 1/2 cup prepared vanilla pudding mix
- 1/4 cup strawberries
- 1/4 cup heavy cream
- 1 tablespoon sugar
- 1 teaspoon vanilla extract

INSTRUCTIONS:

1. Puree strawberries until smooth; mix the pureed strawberries with sugar and set aside.
2. Whip the heavy cream with vanilla extract until soft peaks form; fold the whipped cream and strawberry puree into the vanilla pudding until the mixture is uniform.
3. Refrigerate the mixture for 20 minutes to set before serving.

TIRAMISU PARFAIT

TOTAL TIME: 15 minutes	CALORIES: 902	SERVINGS: 1	CARBS: 52g	PROTEIN: 13g	FATS: 72

INGREDIENTS:

- 1/2 cup mascarpone cheese
- 1/4 cup heavy cream
- 2 tablespoons powdered sugar
- 1/2 teaspoon vanilla extract
- 1/4 cup brewed espresso
- 1/2 cup soft ladyfingers

INSTRUCTIONS:

1. Dip each ladyfinger into espresso soak, about 2 seconds per side, should be soft without disintegrating; arrange on a plate.
2. Whip mascarpone cheese with powdered sugar and vanilla extract until smooth; in a separate bowl, whip heavy cream to soft peaks; fold whipped cream into mascarpone mixture.
3. Layer softened ladyfingers in serving glasses or a bowl; add a layer of mascarpone cream; repeat layers, finishing with a layer of mascarpone cream on top; refrigerate for 20 minutes.

SOFT POACHED PEARS

TOTAL TIME: 30 minutes	CALORIES: 315	SERVINGS: 1	CARBS: 82g	PROTEIN: 1g	FATS: 1g

INGREDIENTS:

- 1 large pear
- 1 cup water
- 1/4 cup sugar
- 1 teaspoon ground cinnamon
- 1/2 teaspoon vanilla extract

INSTRUCTIONS:

1. In a small saucepan, combine water, sugar, cinnamon, and vanilla extract; bring to a simmer.
2. While the syrup heats, peel and core the pear, then cut into halves.
3. Once the syrup is simmering, add the pear; cover and simmer for 18 minutes.
4. Remove from heat, let cool in the syrup for a few minutes; then, using a fork or potato masher, mash the pear to a smooth consistency directly in the syrup.
5. Serve warm or chilled, ensuring the texture is uniformly smooth with no lumps.

CHAPTER 5:
IDDSI LEVEL 5 RECIPES
(MINCED AND MOIST)

STEAMED SPINACH RICOTTA ROLLS

TOTAL TIME: 30 minutes	CALORIES: 609	SERVINGS: 1	CARBS: 100g	PROTEIN: 19g	FATS: 14g

INGREDIENTS:

- 2 cups spinach
- 50g ricotta cheese
- 1 cup all-purpose flour
- 1/2 tablespoon olive oil
- 1 teaspoon baking powder
- 1/4 teaspoon salt
- 1/4 teaspoon garlic powder
- Warm water

INSTRUCTIONS:

1. Steam spinach for 4 minutes; blend into a smooth puree, adding water if necessary.
2. Combine flour, baking powder, and salt in a bowl; add olive oil and spinach puree; mix; gradually add warm water for a soft dough.
3. Mix ricotta with garlic powder in a bowl.
4. Roll out the dough and cut into small pieces; place a spoonful of ricotta on each piece, fold dough over the filling, and seal edges.
5. Set up your steamer; line with parchment if needed; place rolls in the steamer, ensuring they don't touch; steam for 13 minutes until the dough is cooked and firm; enjoy with a suitable sauce or dip; mash if necessary.

MASHED PEAR AND RICOTTA CHEESE TOAST

TOTAL TIME: 15 minutes	CALORIES: 426	SERVINGS: 1	CARBS: 68g	PROTEIN: 14g	FATS: 13g

INGREDIENTS:

- 1 medium pear
- 1/3 cup ricotta cheese
- 1 slice of soft whole wheat bread
- 1/4 cup milk
- 1 tablespoon honey
- 1/4 teaspoon ground cinnamon
- A pinch of salt

INSTRUCTIONS:

1. In a mixing bowl, combine mashed pear, ricotta cheese, honey, cinnamon, and salt; mix until well combined.
2. Pulse bread in a food processor to fine crumbs (<0.1in); in a square mould on a plate, add half the breadcrumbs; moisten with milk; fill mould with the spread, top with remaining breadcrumbs, and moisten again; cover and refrigerate for 1 hour to set.
3. Remove from mould and cut into bite-sized pieces.

MASHED SWEET POTATO AND MAPLE PANCAKES

TOTAL TIME: 30 minutes	CALORIES: 532	SERVINGS: 1	CARBS: 7g	PROTEIN: 15g	FATS: 22g

INGREDIENTS:

- 1 medium sweet potato
- 1/4 cup oat flour or very finely ground oats
- 1/4 cup milk
- 1 tablespoon maple syrup
- 1 teaspoon baking powder
- 1/4 teaspoon cinnamon
- 1 large egg
- 1 tablespoon butter
- Pinch of salt

INSTRUCTIONS:

1. Peel and cut one sweet potato into chunks; boil in water for 17 minutes; drain and blend or mash until smooth.
2. Combine mashed sweet potatoes, milk, maple syrup, melted butter, and egg in a mixing bowl; whisk until thoroughly blended.
3. In another bowl, mix oat flour, baking powder, cinnamon, and salt.
4. Fold dry ingredients into the wet mixture until just combined, ensuring no lumps larger than <0.1in remain.
5. Preheat a non-stick skillet over medium heat; pour small rounds of batter onto the skillet; cook on very low heat for approximately 6 minutes and cover to steam-cook, preventing browning.
6. Use a fork or blender to mash the pancakes further; serve warm with a drizzle of maple syrup and Greek yogurt.

MASHED BERRY PARFAIT WITH SOFT OATS LAYERS

TOTAL TIME: 20 minutes	CALORIES: 309	SERVINGS: 1	CARBS: 56g	PROTEIN: 18g	FATS: 3g

INGREDIENTS:

- 1/2 cup mixed berries (strawberries, raspberries, blueberries)
- 1/3 cup rolled oats
- 1/2 cup Greek yogurt
- 1 tablespoon honey or maple syrup
- 1/4 teaspoon vanilla extract
- 1/2 cup water or milk

INSTRUCTIONS:

1. In a saucepan, cook rolled oats with water or milk and vanilla extract for 10 minutes.
2. Mash mixed berries to a smooth consistency; stir in 1 tablespoon honey or maple syrup if sweetness is desired.
3. In a glass, layer Greek yogurt at the bottom; then add a layer of cooked oats and then a layer of mashed berries; repeat the layers if desired.

APPLE AND SAUSAGE ON ACORN SQUASH BED

TOTAL TIME: 30 minutes	CALORIES: 441	SERVINGS: 1	CARBS: 50g	PROTEIN: 16g	FATS: 22g

INGREDIENTS:

- 1/2 medium acorn squash
- 1 medium chicken sausage
- 1 medium green apple
- 1 tablespoon olive oil
- 1/4 teaspoon cinnamon
- Salt to taste
- 2 tablespoons apple juice

INSTRUCTIONS:

1. Preheat the oven to 350°F; place halved acorn squash on a baking sheet; bake for 25 minutes; mash; mix mashed squash with cinnamon and salt.
2. Meanwhile, cook the sausage in a skillet over medium heat for 10 minutes, then finely mince.
3. Peel, core, and chop the apple into small pieces; place in a saucepan with 2 tablespoons of water; cover and stew over medium heat for 13 minutes, stirring occasionally; remove from heat and mash to a smooth consistency.
4. In a separate bowl, blend minced sausage with olive oil and apple juice.
5. Layer mashed squash in a serving bowl; add the pureed sausage on top; finish with a layer of mashed apple.

MINCED HUEVOS RANCHEROS WITH AVOCADO

TOTAL TIME: 15 minutes	CALORIES: 587	SERVINGS: 1	CARBS: 24g	PROTEIN: 29g	FATS: 46g

INGREDIENTS:

- 2 large eggs
- 1/2 ripe avocado
- 1/4 cup canned refried beans
- 1/4 cup salsa
- 1 tablespoon olive oil
- 1/4 cup cream cheese
- 1/4 cup Greek yogurt

INSTRUCTIONS:

1. Scramble the eggs in olive oil over medium heat until cooked, then mash them to a smooth consistency; warm up the refried beans and mix them with the scrambled eggs to a uniform texture.
2. Strain the salsa to remove any chunks; mix it with the egg and bean mixture; fold in the mashed avocado and add the cream cheese.
3. Serve the huevos rancheros topped with a dollop of Greek yogurt.

CREAMY RICE PUDDING WITH RAISINS

TOTAL TIME: 30 minutes	CALORIES: 593	SERVINGS: 1	CARBS: 102g	PROTEIN: 19g	FATS: 21g

INGREDIENTS:

- 1/4 cup white rice
- 1 1/2 cups water
- 1 1/2 cups whole milk
- 1/4 cup raisins
- 2 tablespoons sugar
- 1/4 teaspoon ground cinnamon
- 1/4 teaspoon salt
- 1 large egg
- 1/2 teaspoon vanilla extract

INSTRUCTIONS:

1. Combine the rinsed rice and water in a saucepan; bring to a boil; reduce heat to low, cover, and simmer for 18 minutes.
2. In a blender, puree the cooked rice with 1 cup of milk until smooth and no grains larger than 0.1in remain; transfer to a pot.
3. Add the remaining 1/2 cup of milk, finely chopped or pureed raisins, sugar, cinnamon, and salt to the pot; cook over medium heat, stirring constantly to prevent sticking, about 13 minutes.
4. Remove from heat; stir in the beaten egg and vanilla extract until fully incorporated.
5. Serve warm, or chill in the refrigerator if preferred cold.

SPICED CARROT AND APPLE PORRIDGE

TOTAL TIME: 20 minutes	CALORIES: 462	SERVINGS: 1	CARBS: 89g	PROTEIN: 11g	FATS: 8g

INGREDIENTS:

- 1/2 cup rolled oats
- 1 cup water
- 1 large carrot
- 1 large apple
- 1/2 cup whole milk
- 1 tablespoon maple syrup
- 1/4 teaspoon ground cinnamon
- Pinch of ground ginger
- Pinch of salt

INSTRUCTIONS:

1. Peel and core one large apple; peel one large carrot; blend both to a smooth puree.
2. In a saucepan, combine oats and water; bring to a boil; reduce heat to simmer; cook for 5 minutes.
3. Stir in pureed carrot and apple; add milk; cook for another 5 minutes, stirring constantly; add maple syrup, cinnamon, ginger, and salt; stir until well combined; continue cooking until mixture reaches a porridge consistency, about 10 minutes.
4. Remove from heat; serve warm.

CREAMY GARLIC AND PARMESAN MUSHROOMS ON TOAST

TOTAL TIME: 20 minutes	CALORIES: 281	SERVINGS: 1	CARBS: 16g	PROTEIN: 11g	FATS: 20g

INGREDIENTS:

- 1/2 cup white mushrooms
- 1 slice of whole wheat bread
- 2 tablespoons Parmesan cheese
- 1 garlic clove
- 1/4 cup whole milk
- 1 tablespoon olive oil
- Salt and pepper to taste

INSTRUCTIONS:

1. Heat olive oil, add minced garlic and finely chopped mushrooms; cook for 5 minutes; add salt, pepper and Parmesan cheese; stir until the mixture becomes smooth; put it into a blender.
2. Pulse bread in a food processor to fine crumbs (<0.1in); in a square mould on a plate, add half the breadcrumbs; moisten with milk; fill mould with the mixture; top with remaining breadcrumbs, and moisten again; cover and refrigerate for 1 hour to set.
3. Remove from mould and cut into bite-sized pieces.

DENVER OMELET MUFFINS

TOTAL TIME: 30 minutes	CALORIES: 259	SERVINGS: 1	CARBS: 6g	PROTEIN: 20g	FATS: 18g

INGREDIENTS:

- 2 large eggs
- 2 tablespoons ham
- 1 tablespoon green bell pepper
- 1 tablespoon raw red bell pepper
- 1 tablespoon onion
- 2 tablespoons milk
- Salt and pepper to taste
- 1 tablespoon cream cheese

INSTRUCTIONS:

1. Preheat your oven to 325°F; grease a muffin tin or use silicone muffin cups for easier removal.
2. Lightly sauté the minced green bell pepper, red bell pepper, ham and onion in a pan over medium heat for 5 minutes.
3. In a bowl, whisk the eggs until smooth; add milk; season with salt and pepper.
4. Stir in the ham, peppers, onion, and cream cheese into the egg mixture, ensuring all pieces are no larger than 0.1in.
5. Pour the egg mixture into two cups of the prepared muffin tin; cover with foil; bake for 18 minutes, or until the eggs are set, avoid crusting.

CREAMY SWEET CORN AND THYME POLENTA

TOTAL TIME: 30 minutes	CALORIES: 563	SERVINGS: 1	CARBS: 77g	PROTEIN: 16g	FATS: 21g

INGREDIENTS:

- 1 cup of canned corn
- Water or vegetable broth
- 1/2 cup polenta
- 2 cups water
- 1/2 teaspoon salt
- 1 tablespoon butter
- 1 teaspoon fresh thyme leaves
- 1/4 cup grated Parmesan cheese

INSTRUCTIONS:

1. Blend the corn on high until completely smooth; pass the puree through a fine-mesh strainer or sieve to remove any remaining skins.
2. In a saucepan, bring 2 cups of water and 1/2 teaspoon of salt to a boil; whisk in the polenta; reduce heat to low and cook, stirring frequently, for 18 minutes; stir in the butter, fresh thyme leaves, and grated Parmesan cheese until well combined.
3. Incorporate the smooth corn puree into the polenta, stirring until thoroughly mixed and ensuring there are no lumps larger than 0.1in; cook for an additional 5 minutes; serve warm.

CREAMY BUTTERNUT SQUASH PORRIDGE

TOTAL TIME: 20 minutes	CALORIES: 91	SERVINGS: 1	CARBS: 91g	PROTEIN: 39g	FATS: 40g

INGREDIENTS:

- 1 cup butternut squash
- 1/2 cup rolled oats
- 1 1/2 cups milk
- 1/4 teaspoon cinnamon
- 1 tablespoon maple syrup
- 1 tablespoon unsalted butter
- Pinch of salt
- Banana or apple puree

INSTRUCTIONS:

1. Combine the peeled and diced butternut squash, milk, and a pinch of salt in a saucepan; bring to a boil; reduce heat, simmer for 15 minutes.
2. Add rolled oats and cinnamon; cook for 5 more minutes; remove from heat; stir in butter and maple syrup until fully incorporated; use a blender to puree the mixture to a smooth consistency.
3. Serve warm with optional toppings of mashed banana or apple puree.

MAIN COURSE

SAUSAGE GRAVY OVER CREAMY CAULIFLOWER PUREE

TOTAL TIME: 30 minutes	CALORIES: 522	SERVINGS: 1	CARBS: 27g	PROTEIN: 22g	FATS: 31g

INGREDIENTS:

- 1/2 cauliflower
- 1 chicken sausage
- 1/4 cup milk
- 1 tablespoon cornstarch
- 1 tablespoon olive oil
- 1/4 cup chicken broth
- Salt and pepper to taste
- 1/8 teaspoon dried thyme

INSTRUCTIONS:

1. Steam cauliflower for 20 minutes; puree with milk until smooth; season with salt and pepper.
2. Cook sausage in olive oil over medium heat for 10 minutes; finely mince.
3. Dissolve cornstarch in chicken broth; add to sausage in pan; season with thyme; stir for 5 minutes.
4. Plate by spooning cauliflower puree, then ladle sausage gravy on top.

MINCED CHICKEN WITH OLIVE TAPENADE

TOTAL TIME: 25 minutes	CALORIES: 556	SERVINGS: 1	CARBS: 14g	PROTEIN: 27g	FATS: 47g

INGREDIENTS:

- 1 medium-sized chicken breast
- 2 cups water
- 10 pitted olives
- 1 tablespoon capers
- 2 garlic cloves
- 1 small bunch of fresh parsley
- 2 tablespoons olive oil
- 1/4 medium lemon
- 1/2 medium-sized ripe avocado
- Salt and pepper to taste

INSTRUCTIONS:

1. Poach chicken breast in simmering water for 15 minutes; cool slightly and mince.
2. Blend olives, capers, garlic, parsley, lemon juice, and 1 tablespoon olive oil to make tapenade.
3. Mash avocado with remaining olive oil, salt, and pepper until smooth.
4. Combine minced chicken with olive tapenade and mashed avocado; mix well;
5. Check consistency; if too thick, adjust by adding a teaspoon of water at a time until desired moistness is achieved.

CREAMY POLENTA WITH MINCED ROAST VEGETABLES

TOTAL TIME: 30 minutes	CALORIES: 253	SERVINGS: 1	CARBS: 29g	PROTEIN: 6g	FATS: 13g

INGREDIENTS:

- 1/4 medium zucchini
- 1/4 medium yellow bell pepper
- 1/4 medium red bell pepper
- 1/4 medium eggplant
- 1/2 tablespoon olive oil
- 3 tablespoons polenta
- 3/4 cup water
- 1 teaspoon unsalted butter
- Salt to taste
- 1 tablespoon grated Parmesan cheese

INSTRUCTIONS:

1. Preheat the oven to 425°F; peel and chop zucchini, bell peppers, and eggplant into large pieces; toss with olive oil and a pinch of salt; roast for 20 minutes.
2. Boil water in a pot; slowly pour in polenta while stirring; reduce heat and simmer until thick, stirring constantly, about 15 minutes; stir in butter and Parmesan cheese until smooth.
3. Remove vegetables from the oven; finely mince while still warm to a smooth consistency ensuring no pieces larger than 0.1in.
4. Thoroughly mix minced vegetables with polenta for a uniform texture.

HERBED VEAL AND MUSHROOM MASH

TOTAL TIME: 30 minutes	CALORIES: 314	SERVINGS: 1	CARBS: 2g	PROTEIN: 33g	FATS: 18g

INGREDIENTS:

- 200g veal cutlet
- 4 white button mushrooms
- 1 sprig fresh rosemary
- 1 sprig fresh thyme
- 1 tablespoon olive oil
- Salt and pepper to taste

INSTRUCTIONS:

1. Simmer veal in water for 15 minutes; drain; mince finely.
2. Sauté mushrooms in olive oil with rosemary and thyme for 5 minutes; remove herbs; mince mushrooms.
3. Combine minced veal and mushrooms; season with salt and pepper; mix until uniform and smooth.

MINCED LAMB GYRO WITH TZATZIKI

TOTAL TIME: 30 minutes	CALORIES: 427	SERVINGS: 1	CARBS: 9g	PROTEIN: 36g	FATS: 26g

INGREDIENTS:

- 200g lamb steak
- 2 cups water
- 1/2 large cucumber
- 1 clove garlic
- 100g Greek yogurt
- 1 teaspoon olive oil
- 1/2 teaspoon dried dill
- 1 teaspoon lemon juice
- Salt and pepper to taste

INSTRUCTIONS:

1. Simmer lamb steak in a pot of boiling water for 20 minutes; remove and cool slightly; finely mince to a smooth consistency.
2. Grate cucumber, squeeze out excess water; mince garlic clove.
3. Combine Greek yogurt, olive oil, minced garlic, dried dill, lemon juice, salt, and pepper; stir until smooth for tzatziki sauce.
4. Mix minced lamb with tzatziki sauce until well-integrated and moist.

PORK SOUVLAKI WITH GARLIC SAUCE AND HERB POTATOES

TOTAL TIME: 30 minutes	CALORIES: 1353	SERVINGS: 1	CARBS: 72g	PROTEIN: 160g	FATS: 45g

INGREDIENTS:

- 200g pork tenderloin
- 3 cloves of garlic
- 100g Greek yogurt
- 1 small lemon
- 1 tablespoon olive oil
- 1 teaspoon dried oregano
- 2 medium potatoes
- 1 tablespoon butter
- 1 teaspoon dried basil
- 1/4 cup milk
- Salt and pepper to taste

INSTRUCTIONS:

1. Boil the peeled potatoes in salted water for 20 minutes; drain; add butter and milk; mash until smooth; stir in dried basil, salt and pepper.
2. Simmer pork tenderloin in water for 20 minutes; remove and cool slightly; finely mince to a paste.
3. Peel and mince garlic cloves; mix with Greek yogurt, juice from the lemon, olive oil, oregano, salt, and pepper to make sauce.
4. Combine pork puree with half of the garlic sauce; serve potatoes on the side.

BAKED HALIBUT WITH FENNEL

TOTAL TIME: 30 minutes	CALORIES: 543	SERVINGS: 1	CARBS: 20g	PROTEIN: 45g	FATS: 33g

INGREDIENTS:

- 1 halibut filet
- 1 fennel bulb
- 2 tablespoons olive oil
- 1/2 lemon
- 1 teaspoon dried thyme
- Salt and pepper to taste

INSTRUCTIONS:

1. Preheat the oven to 375°F; lightly oil halibut; season with salt, pepper, thyme; bake for 15 minutes.
2. Trim and chop the fennel bulb; boil for 15 minutes; drain; puree with olive oil and lemon juice until smooth.
3. Check halibut for bones; finely mince the cooked fish.
4. Plate minced halibut; side with fennel puree.

TURKEY MEATBALLS AND SPINACH KOFTA MASH

TOTAL TIME: 30 minutes	CALORIES: 512	SERVINGS: 1	CARBS: 43g	PROTEIN: 65g	FATS: 8g

INGREDIENTS:

- 200g turkey breast
- 1 medium potato
- 1 large handful of fresh spinach leaves
- 2 tablespoons plain Greek yogurt
- 1 teaspoon lemon juice
- 1 teaspoon olive oil
- 1/4 teaspoon garlic powder
- 1/4 teaspoon onion powder
- Salt and pepper to taste

INSTRUCTIONS:

1. Boil turkey breast for 20 minutes; drain and allow to cool slightly; finely mince or puree to a smooth paste.
2. Boil the peeled potato chunks in salted water for 20 minutes; mash.
3. Steam spinach for 3 minutes; puree to a smooth consistency.
4. In a bowl, combine Greek yogurt with lemon juice, olive oil, garlic powder, onion powder, salt, and pepper; whisk until smooth for sauce.
5. Mix the turkey puree with the spinach puree and mashed potato; form them into loose balls on the plate using a spoon or ice cream scoop; do not compress; top with the yogurt sauce.

SEAFOOD CHOWDER SOUP

TOTAL TIME: 30 minutes	CALORIES: 837	SERVINGS: 1	CARBS: 52g	PROTEIN: 32g	FATS: 56g

INGREDIENTS:

- 1 small haddock
- 4 medium shrimp
- 1 small potato
- 1/2 medium onion
- 1 small carrot
- 2 cups vegetable broth
- 1/2 cup heavy cream
- 1 tablespoon unsalted butter
- 1 bay leaf
- Salt and pepper to taste

INSTRUCTIONS:

1. Peel and dice potato and carrot into small pieces; finely chop onion; simmer vegetables in broth with bay leaf for 15 minutes.
2. Add haddock and shrimp to pot; cook for 5 minutes; remove bay leaf.
3. Puree soup mixture using immersion blender until smooth, ensuring no piece larger than 0.1in remains; stir in heavy cream and butter; heat through; season with salt and pepper.

SOFT TOFU AND COTTAGE CHEESE BROCCOLI BAKE

TOTAL TIME: 30 minutes	CALORIES: 584	SERVINGS: 1	CARBS: 30g	PROTEIN: 41g	FATS: 36g

INGREDIENTS:

- 1/2 block soft tofu
- 1/2 head broccoli
- 1/3 cup cottage cheese
- 1 tablespoon olive oil
- 1 clove garlic
- 1/4 cup cheddar cheese
- Salt and pepper to taste
- 1 slice whole wheat bread

INSTRUCTIONS:

1. Preheat the oven to 375°F; steam broccoli for 7 minutes.
2. In a pan, sauté minced garlic in olive oil for 2 minutes.
3. In a bowl, mash tofu and steamed broccoli together; stir in sautéed garlic, cottage cheese, salt, and pepper into the tofu-broccoli mixture.
4. Remove the crusts and pulse bread in a food processor, mix into the tofu-broccoli blend.
5. Transfer to an oven-safe dish, sprinkle with cheese; cover with foil; bake for 15 minutes or until the cheese melts; remove from oven, let cool for 2 minutes, then mash again to ensure a consistent, moist texture.

MINCED MEATLOAF WITH KETCHUP GLAZE AND PARSNIP PUREE

TOTAL TIME: 30 minutes	CALORIES: 1628	SERVINGS: 1	CARBS: 12g	PROTEIN: 74g	FATS: 94g

INGREDIENTS:

- 200g minced beef
- 1 small carrot
- 1 small zucchini
- 2 medium eggs
- 1 slice whole wheat bread
- 4 tablespoons ketchup
- 2 tablespoons brown sugar
- 1 teaspoon Worcestershire sauce
- 1/2 teaspoon garlic powder
- 2 medium parsnips
- 2 tablespoons butter
- 1/4 cup milk
- Salt and pepper to taste
- 2 tablespoons olive oil

INSTRUCTIONS:

1. Preheat the oven to 375°F; mix beef, grated carrot and zucchini, eggs, pureed breadcrumbs, salt, and pepper in a bowl; shape mixture into a loaf; heat olive oil in a pan; sear the loaf on all sides for 5 minutes.
2. Stir together ketchup, brown sugar, Worcestershire sauce, and garlic powder for glaze; spread half of the glaze over the meatloaf; cover with foil; bake for 20 minutes.
3. Boil the chopped parsnips for 15 minutes; drain; add butter and milk; puree in a blender; stir in salt and pepper.
4. Remove the meatloaf, spread the remaining glaze on top, and bake for 5 more minutes.
5. Mash thoroughly; mix in a small amount of warm broth if more moisture is needed; serve with parsnip on the side.

GARLIC SHRIMP AND MASHED POTATOES

TOTAL TIME: 30 minutes	CALORIES: 660	SERVINGS: 1	CARBS: 67g	PROTEIN: 18g	FATS: 37g

INGREDIENTS:

- 1 large potato
- 6 large shrimp
- 3 cloves of garlic
- 2 tablespoons heavy cream
- 1 tablespoon butter
- 1 tablespoon olive oil
- Salt and pepper to taste

INSTRUCTIONS:

1. Peel and boil potato for 20 minutes; mash with cream, butter, salt, and pepper until smooth.
2. Mince garlic; peel, devein and sauté the shrimps with olive oil and half of the garlic over medium heat for 3 minutes each side; mince or pulse the cooked shrimps.
3. Fold the shrimps into mashed potatoes; add remaining garlic.

FETA, WHITE BEANS AND OLIVE POLENTA MASH

TOTAL TIME: 30 minutes	CALORIES: 453	SERVINGS: 1	CARBS: 48g	PROTEIN: 13g	FATS: 25g

INGREDIENTS:

- 1/4 cup polenta
- 1 cup water
- 1 clove garlic
- 3 tablespoons feta cheese
- 1/4 cup canned white beans
- 3 black olives
- 2 tablespoons olive oil
- 1/4 lemon
- 1 small tomato
- A small handful of parsley
- Salt and pepper to taste

INSTRUCTIONS:

1. Cook polenta with water and a pinch of salt, stir constantly for 5 minutes.
2. Sauté garlic in 1 tablespoon olive oil for 1 minute.
3. Combine polenta, garlic, crumbled feta, white beans, and chopped olives in a bowl; mash mixture until smooth and fully integrated; stir in lemon juice, olive oil, chopped parsley, salt, pepper, peeled and diced tomato.

MINCED COD WITH TOMATO SAUCE AND MASHED PEAS

TOTAL TIME: 30 minutes	CALORIES: 452	SERVINGS: 1	CARBS: 27g	PROTEIN: 50g	FATS: 15g

INGREDIENTS:

- 1 cod filet
- 1 medium tomato
- 1 cup frozen peas
- 1 tablespoon olive oil
- 1 clove garlic
- 1/4 teaspoon dried oregano
- 1/4 teaspoon dried basil
- Salt and pepper to taste

INSTRUCTIONS:

1. Preheat the oven to 350°F; wrap cod filet in foil with a drizzle of olive oil, salt, and pepper; bake for 20 minutes until flaky.
2. Simmer peas in water for 15 minutes; drain.
3. Sauté garlic in olive oil until fragrant; blend garlic with peeled tomato, oregano, basil, salt, and pepper until smooth.
4. Mash baked cod and peas together until achieving a consistent texture.
5. Combine mashed cod and peas with tomato sauce; serve warm.

MASHED BEAN AND VEGETABLE CASSOULET

TOTAL TIME: 30 minutes	CALORIES: 829	SERVINGS: 1	CARBS: 94g	PROTEIN: 38g	FATS: 36g

INGREDIENTS:

- 1 cup canned white beans
- 1 small carrot
- 1 medium zucchini
- 2 tablespoons olive oil
- 1 small onion
- 2 cloves garlic
- 1 small leek
- 1 sprig thyme leaves
- 1 small tomato
- 3 cups spinach
- Salt and pepper to taste
- 5 tablespoons grated Parmesan cheese

INSTRUCTIONS:

1. Preheat the oven to 375°F; rinse beans; boil peeled carrot and zucchini for 15 minutes.
2. Sauté onion and garlic in olive oil until translucent, about 3 minutes; finely chop leek (white part only) and peeled tomato, add to the pan, cook for another 2 minutes.
3. Drain and mash carrots and zucchini; mix in onion, garlic, leek, and tomato.
4. Puree spinach and thyme; fold into mash.
5. Transfer to an oven-proof dish, top with Parmesan, cover with foil, bake for 10 minutes.

CREAMY CHICKEN, GARLIC MUSHROOMS WITH CARROT PUREE

TOTAL TIME: 30 minutes	CALORIES: 918	SERVINGS: 1	CARBS: 23g	PROTEIN: 59g	FATS: 66g

INGREDIENTS:

- 1 medium chicken breast
- 5 button mushrooms
- 2 large carrots
- 4 cloves garlic
- 2 tablespoons unsalted butter
- 1 tablespoon olive oil
- 1/4 cup cooking cream
- Salt and pepper to taste
- 1 teaspoon fresh thyme
- 1 cup chicken stock

INSTRUCTIONS:

1. Boil carrots in water for 20 minutes; drain, puree with a blender, season with salt; set aside.
2. Poach chicken breast in chicken stock for 15 minutes; shred with forks; blend to desired consistency.
3. Sauté minced garlic in olive oil for 1 minute; add finely chopped mushrooms; cook for 5 minutes.
4. Combine chicken, mashed mushroom, butter, and cream in a pan; warm through and mix to a smooth consistency; season with salt and pepper.
5. Layer chicken and mushroom mix over carrot puree in a bowl.

MINCED BEEF AND EGGPLANT PUREE

TOTAL TIME: 30 minutes	CALORIES: 883	SERVINGS: 1	CARBS: 40g	PROTEIN: 37g	FATS: 66g

INGREDIENTS:

- 200g ground beef
- 1 large eggplant
- 2 tablespoons olive oil
- 1 small onion
- 2 cloves garlic
- 1/4 teaspoon ground cinnamon
- Salt and pepper to taste
- 1/4 cup beef stock
- 2 tablespoons Parmesan cheese

INSTRUCTIONS:

1. Peel eggplant, cut into cubes; steam for 10 minutes.
2. Sauté onion and garlic in olive oil until translucent; add minced beef and cinnamon; cook until browned;
3. Combine steamed eggplant, cooked beef mixture in a blender; add beef stock to achieve a smooth, cohesive consistency.
4. Season with salt and pepper; stir in grated cheese.

SALMON, HERBED GOAT CHEESE AND BEET MASH WITH GREEK YOGURT

TOTAL TIME: 30 minutes	CALORIES: 763	SERVINGS: 1	CARBS: 10g	PROTEIN: 49g	FATS: 58g

INGREDIENTS:

- 1 medium beet
- 1 salmon filet
- 2 tablespoons goat cheese
- 2 tablespoons Greek yogurt
- 2 tablespoons olive oil
- 1/2 teaspoon dried thyme
- 1/2 teaspoon dried rosemary
- Salt and pepper to taste

INSTRUCTIONS:

1. Peel and chop the beet; boil for 20 minutes.
2. Heat 1 tablespoon of olive oil in a pan over medium heat; cook the salmon filet for 4 minutes on each side.
3. Drain the beet; blend with olive oil until smooth using a food processor; add goat cheese and Greek yogurt to the beet puree; blend.
4. Season the beet with dried thyme, rosemary, salt, and pepper; serve it topped with the salmon filet.

STUFFED PEPPER PUREE WITH MINCED TURKEY

TOTAL TIME: 30 minutes	CALORIES: 705	SERVINGS: 1	CARBS: 22g	PROTEIN: 24g	FATS: 59g

INGREDIENTS:

- 1 large bell pepper
- 150g ground turkey
- 1 small onion
- 2 cloves garlic
- 1 small tomato
- 2 tablespoons olive oil
- 1/2 teaspoon smoked paprika
- Salt and pepper to taste
- 1 tablespoon cream cheese

INSTRUCTIONS:

1. Core, peel and finely chop bell pepper; steam for 10 minutes.
2. Heat olive oil in a pan; sauté onion and garlic for 3 minutes; add minced turkey to the pan; cook for 5 minutes; mix in smoked paprika, salt, and pepper; add peeled and chopped tomatoes; simmer for 10 minutes.
3. In a dish, layer the chopped bell peppers, turkey, and tomatoes; dot cream cheese on top.

MINCED ORANGE GLAZED CHICKEN WITH CREAMY SPINACH PUREE

TOTAL TIME: 30 minutes	CALORIES: 687	SERVINGS: 1	CARBS: 33g	PROTEIN: 65g	FATS: 35g

INGREDIENTS:

- 1 large chicken breast
- 2 large handfuls of spinach
- 1 small orange
- 1 tablespoon honey
- 1 tablespoon olive oil
- 1 clove garlic
- 2 tablespoons heavy cream
- Salt and pepper to taste
- 1/4 cup chicken stock
- Fresh dill

INSTRUCTIONS:

1. Poach chicken breast in simmering water for 15 minutes; then mince finely.
2. Steam spinach for 5 minutes; blend to puree; add heavy cream; season with salt and pepper.
3. In a saucepan, combine orange juice, zest, honey; reduce to a thick glaze, about 5 minutes.
4. Sauté garlic in olive oil until fragrant; mix with minced chicken and orange glaze; blend to smooth consistency.
5. Combine chicken and spinach mixtures; add chicken stock to reach smooth consistency; garnish with finely chopped dill; serve warm.

MASHED CHICKPEA AND ROASTED VEGETABLE BOWL

TOTAL TIME: 30 minutes	CALORIES: 578	SERVINGS: 1	CARBS: 61g	PROTEIN: 18g	FATS: 33g

INGREDIENTS:

- 1 can chickpeas
- 1 large carrot
- 1 medium zucchini
- 2 tablespoons olive oil
- 1/2 teaspoon garlic powder
- 1/2 teaspoon onion powder
- Salt and pepper to taste
- 1/4 cup vegetable stock
- Fresh parsley

INSTRUCTIONS:

1. Preheat the oven to 400°F; add a small amount of stock in the roasting tray; cover with foil and roast carrot and zucchini for 20 minutes.
2. Blend chickpeas, roasted vegetables and olive oil in the food processor until smooth.
3. Add garlic powder, onion powder, salt, pepper; adjust consistency with vegetable stock.
4. Garnish with finely chopped parsley; serve warm.

MINTED ZUCCHINI AND LAMB PUREE

TOTAL TIME: 30 minutes	CALORIES: 772	SERVINGS: 1	CARBS: 19g	PROTEIN: 33g	FATS: 64g

INGREDIENTS:

- 150g ground lamb
- 2 medium zucchinis
- 10 fresh mint leaves
- 2 tablespoons olive oil
- 1/2 medium onion
- 1 clove garlic
- Salt and pepper to taste
- 1/4 teaspoon ground cumin
- 2 tablespoons plain Greek yogurt

INSTRUCTIONS:

1. Sauté onion and garlic in olive oil until translucent, about 3 minutes; add ground lamb, cumin, salt, and pepper; cook until browned, about 7 minutes.
2. Blend cooked lamb, sautéed onion and garlic, and fresh mint leaves until smooth.
3. Steam zucchinis until very soft, about 7 minutes; blend into a smooth puree.
4. Combine lamb and zucchini purees; add Greek yogurt on top.

ROASTED RED BEET AND GREEK YOGURT BLEND WITH DILL

TOTAL TIME: 30 minutes	CALORIES: 243	SERVINGS: 1	CARBS: 18g	PROTEIN: 12g	FATS: 100g

INGREDIENTS:

- 1 large red beet
- 100g Greek yogurt
- 3 sprigs fresh dill
- 1 tablespoon olive oil
- 1/4 teaspoon garlic powder
- Salt and pepper to taste

INSTRUCTIONS:

1. Wrap beet in foil, roast at 400°F for 25 minutes.
2. Peel beet while warm, chop finely; blend beet to a smooth puree with olive oil, salt, and pepper.
3. Mix Greek yogurt with garlic powder, minced dill, salt, and pepper.
4. Combine beet puree with yogurt mixture until smooth; add olive oil if needed for smoothness.

WHIPPED RICOTTA WITH SUN-DRIED TOMATOES

TOTAL TIME: 15 minutes	CALORIES: 532	SERVINGS: 1	CARBS: 20g	PROTEIN: 26g	FATS: 116g

INGREDIENTS:

- 200g ricotta cheese
- 5 sun-dried tomatoes
- 1 tablespoon olive oil
- 1 clove garlic
- 1/4 teaspoon salt
- 1/4 teaspoon black pepper
- 3 basil leaves

INSTRUCTIONS:

1. Finely mince sun-dried tomatoes and garlic.
2. Combine ricotta, minced sun-dried tomatoes, minced garlic, olive oil, salt, and pepper in a bowl; blend until smooth with a food processor; stir in minced basil leaves.

ROASTED CARROT AND CUMIN SPREAD

TOTAL TIME: 30 minutes	CALORIES: 208	SERVINGS: 1	CARBS: 19g	PROTEIN: 4g	FATS: 100g

INGREDIENTS:

- 2 medium carrots
- 1 tablespoon olive oil
- 1/2 teaspoon ground cumin
- Salt and pepper to taste
- 2 tablespoons plain Greek yogurt
- 1 teaspoon honey
- 1 teaspoon lemon juice

INSTRUCTIONS:

1. Peel carrots, chop finely; roast carrots with olive oil and cumin at 400°F for 20 minutes; puree roasted carrots until smooth.
2. Combine carrot puree with Greek yogurt, honey, lemon juice, salt, and pepper.
3. Blend until mixture reaches desired consistency.

BROCCOLI WITH FETA AND DILL

TOTAL TIME: 20 minutes	CALORIES: 183	SERVINGS: 1	CARBS: 12g	PROTEIN: 8g	FATS: 13g

INGREDIENTS:

- 1/2 large broccoli
- 25g feta cheese
- 1/2 tablespoon olive oil
- 2 sprigs fresh dill
- Salt and pepper to taste
- 1/2 teaspoon lemon zest
- 1/2 tablespoon lemon juice

INSTRUCTIONS:

1. Steam broccoli florets for 7 minutes; mash it with olive oil, lemon zest, lemon juice, salt, and pepper until smooth.
2. Crumble feta cheese, blend into the broccoli mixture; stir in minced dill.
3. Check consistency, add olive oil if needed for smoothness.

CAULIFLOWER TAHINI WITH GREEN OLIVES

TOTAL TIME: 20 minutes	CALORIES: 359	SERVINGS: 1	CARBS: 29g	PROTEIN: 12g	FATS: 169g

INGREDIENTS:

- 1 small cauliflower head
- 1 tablespoon tahini
- 6 green olives
- 1 tablespoon olive oil
- Salt and pepper to taste
- 1/4 teaspoon garlic powder
- 1 tablespoon lemon juice

INSTRUCTIONS:

1. Steam cauliflower for 15 minutes; mash cauliflower with tahini, olive oil, garlic powder, salt, and pepper until smooth.
2. Finely chop green olives, stir into cauliflower mixture.
3. Stir in lemon juice, check for smooth, mashed consistency.

LENTILS WITH CORIANDER AND OLIVE OIL

TOTAL TIME: 25 minutes	CALORIES: 621	SERVINGS: 1	CARBS: 62g	PROTEIN: 31g	FATS: 101g

INGREDIENTS:

- 100g red lentils
- 2 tablespoons olive oil
- 1/2 teaspoon ground coriander
- Salt and pepper to taste
- 1/4 teaspoon garlic powder
- 1 tablespoon fresh lemon juice
- 1/4 teaspoon turmeric powder
- 3 tablespoons Greek yogurt

INSTRUCTIONS:

1. Rinse lentils thoroughly; boil lentils for 20 minutes.
2. Drain lentils; mash with olive oil, garlic powder, turmeric, salt, and pepper until smooth.
3. Stir in ground coriander and lemon juice; mix in Greek yogurt to achieve creamy consistency.

CREAMY AVOCADO AND FETA MASH WITH DILL

TOTAL TIME: 10 minutes	CALORIES: 439	SERVINGS: 1	CARBS: 14g	PROTEIN: 7g	FATS: 136g

INGREDIENTS:

- 1 avocado
- 30g feta cheese
- 1 tablespoon olive oil
- 3 sprigs fresh dill
- Salt and pepper to taste
- 1 teaspoon lemon juice

INSTRUCTIONS:

1. Halve the avocado, remove the pit, scoop out the flesh.
2. Crumble the feta cheese.
3. Combine avocado, crumbled feta, olive oil, lemon juice, salt, and pepper in a bowl; mash the mixture until smooth with no lumps; mix in finely chopped dill.

PEAR AND RICOTTA CREAM WITH CINNAMON

TOTAL TIME: 15 minutes	CALORIES: 282	SERVINGS: 1	CARBS: 54g	PROTEIN: 7g	FATS: 13g

INGREDIENTS:

- 1 large pear
- 3 tablespoons ricotta cheese
- 1/2 teaspoon ground cinnamon
- 1 tablespoon honey
- 1 teaspoon lemon juice

INSTRUCTIONS:

1. Peel pear, core, and chop finely.
2. Steam pear pieces for 10 minutes; mash pear with ricotta cheese, cinnamon, honey, and lemon juice until smooth.
3. Check consistency, adjust sweetness if needed.

APRICOT AND MASCARPONE BLEND WITH HONEY

TOTAL TIME: 15 minutes	CALORIES: 329	SERVINGS: 1	CARBS: 30	PROTEIN: 3g	FATS: 42g

INGREDIENTS:

- 3 fresh apricots
- 50g mascarpone cheese
- 1 tablespoon honey
- 1/2 teaspoon vanilla extract
- 1/4 teaspoon ground cinnamon

INSTRUCTIONS:

1. Halve apricots, remove pits, and chop finely.
2. Steam chopped apricots for 10 minutes.
3. Mash steamed apricots with mascarpone cheese, honey, vanilla extract, and cinnamon until smooth.
4. Check consistency, adjust sweetness if needed.

APPLE WITH CINNAMON AND CREAM CHEESE

TOTAL TIME: 20 minutes	CALORIES: 333	SERVINGS: 1	CARBS: 45g	PROTEIN: 4g	FATS: 34g

INGREDIENTS:

- 1 large apple
- 50g cream cheese
- 1/2 teaspoon ground cinnamon
- 1 tablespoon brown sugar
- 1 teaspoon vanilla extract
- 1 teaspoon water

INSTRUCTIONS:

1. Peel and core the apple, chop into small pieces.
2. Stew apple pieces with cinnamon, brown sugar, vanilla extract, and water for 15 minutes.
3. Mash stewed apple and mix in cream cheese until smooth.

CREAMY PEANUT BUTTER AND BANANA PUREE

TOTAL TIME: 10 minutes	CALORIES: 321	SERVINGS: 1	CARBS: 40g	PROTEIN: 10g	FATS: 51g

INGREDIENTS:

- 1 ripe banana
- 2 tablespoons peanut butter
- 1 teaspoon honey
- Pinch of ground cinnamon
- 1 tablespoon milk

INSTRUCTIONS:

1. Peel the banana and combine it with peanut butter, honey, and cinnamon in a bowl.
2. Puree mixture until completely smooth.
3. Stir in milk to reach desired consistency, ensuring no lumps remain.

RED BEAN AND RICE PUREE WITH MILD SALSA

TOTAL TIME: 15 minutes	CALORIES: 291	SERVINGS: 1	CARBS: 35g	PROTEIN: 8g	FATS: 14g

INGREDIENTS:

- 70g canned red beans
- 20g white rice
- 2 tablespoons mild salsa
- 1 tablespoon olive oil
- Salt and pepper to taste
- 1/2 teaspoon lime juice
- 1/4 teaspoon ground cumin

INSTRUCTIONS:

1. Rinse the white rice; cook it in boiling water for 15 minutes; drain well.
2. Rinse red beans; blend them with cooked rice, mild salsa, olive oil, cumin, salt, and pepper until smooth.
3. Add lime juice, stir into the puree; heat gently if required.

DESSERTS

MINT CHOCOLATE CHIP WHIP

TOTAL TIME: 30 minutes	CALORIES: 686	SERVINGS: 1	CARBS: 47g	PROTEIN: 7g	FATS: 58g

INGREDIENTS:

- 1 large avocado
- 1 tablespoon honey
- 2 tablespoons mint leaves
- 1 tablespoon cocoa powder
- 15g dark chocolate
- 1/4 cup heavy cream

INSTRUCTIONS:

1. 1. Peel, pit, and mash avocado until smooth; blend in honey, minced mint, and cocoa powder until fully incorporated.
2. 2. Gently fold in melted dark chocolate; ensure no hard pieces remain, blend until mixture is uniform and creamy.
3. 3. Whip heavy cream to soft peaks; fold into avocado-chocolate mixture until smooth and light.
4. 4. Serve immediately or chill if a colder texture is desired; garnish with chocolate shavings before serving.

ESPRESSO BROWNIE MOUSSE

TOTAL TIME: 20 minutes	CALORIES: 471	SERVINGS: 1	CARBS: 37g	PROTEIN: 5g	FATS: 35g

INGREDIENTS:

- 1/2 medium avocado
- 1 tablespoon espresso powder
- 1/2 tablespoon unsweetened cocoa powder
- 2 teaspoons honey
- 1/2 teaspoon vanilla extract
- 1/4 dark chocolate bar
- 2 tablespoons heavy cream

INSTRUCTIONS:

1. Combine avocado, dissolved espresso, cocoa powder, honey, vanilla extract; mash until smooth.
2. Fold in melted chocolate; incorporate whipped cream; achieve uniform, mousse-like consistency.
3. Chill in the refrigerator for 15 minutes.

BANANA FOSTER PUREE

TOTAL TIME: 15 minutes	CALORIES: 384	SERVINGS: 1	CARBS: 44g	PROTEIN: 2g	FATS: 17g

INGREDIENTS:

- 1 medium banana
- 1/2 tablespoon unsalted butter
- 1 tablespoon dark brown sugar
- 1/4 teaspoon ground cinnamon
- 1 tablespoon dark rum, optional
- 1/4 teaspoon vanilla extract
- 1 tablespoon orange juice
- 2 tablespoons heavy cream

INSTRUCTIONS:

1. Peel, slice banana; use fork to mash until smooth.
2. Melt butter in pan; add brown sugar, cinnamon; stir until dissolved; add mashed banana, rum or rum extract, vanilla extract; stir for 5 minutes.
3. Remove from heat; blend in orange juice.
4. Let mixture cool slightly; blend in heavy cream until fully incorporated.

MANGO COCONUT CREAM

TOTAL TIME: 15 minutes	CALORIES: 388	SERVINGS: 1	CARBS: 61g	PROTEIN: 14g	FATS: 14g

INGREDIENTS:

- 1 medium mango
- 1/4 cup coconut milk
- 1 teaspoon honey
- 1/8 teaspoon ground ginger
- 1 tablespoon lime juice
- 1/8 teaspoon ground cardamom
- 2 tablespoons Greek yogurt

INSTRUCTIONS:

1. Puree mango until smooth.
2. Mix coconut milk, honey, ginger, lime juice, cardamom; blend well with mango; stir in Greek yogurt.
3. Chill in the refrigerator for 10 minutes.

CARAMEL APPLE WHIP

TOTAL TIME: 25 minutes	CALORIES: 266	SERVINGS: 1	CARBS: 31g	PROTEIN: 1g	FATS: 17g

INGREDIENTS:

- 1 small apple
- 1 tablespoon unsalted butter
- 2 teaspoons brown sugar
- Pinch of ground cinnamon
- 1/8 teaspoon vanilla extract
- 1 tablespoon water
- 2 tablespoons whipped cream

INSTRUCTIONS:

1. Peel and dice the apple; cook with butter, sugar, cinnamon, vanilla and water until soft, for about 12 minutes.
2. Puree apple mixture until smooth; cool to room temperature.
3. Fold whipped cream into apple mixture; chill for 10 minutes; serve.

STRAWBERRY CHEESECAKE FLUFF

TOTAL TIME: 20 minutes	CALORIES: 343	SERVINGS: 1	CARBS: 23g	PROTEIN: 5g	FATS: 26g

INGREDIENTS:

- 4 strawberries
- 1/4 block cream cheese
- 1 tablespoon icing sugar
- 1/2 teaspoon lemon juice
- 1/8 teaspoon vanilla extract
- 1 tablespoon whipped cream

INSTRUCTIONS:

1. Purée the strawberries.
2. Blend the cream cheese, icing sugar, lemon juice, and vanilla until smooth.
3. Combine the strawberry purée and the cream cheese mixture; whip to fluff.
4. Fold in the whipped cream; chill for 10 minutes.

SNICKERDOODLE DOUGH MASH

TOTAL TIME: 10 minutes	CALORIES: 181	SERVINGS: 1	CARBS: 29	PROTEIN: 3g	FATS: 8g

INGREDIENTS:

- 1 small banana
- 1 tablespoon almond flour
- 1/4 teaspoon ground cinnamon
- 1 teaspoon brown sugar
- Pinch of cream of tartar
- 1/8 teaspoon vanilla extract
- 2 teaspoons unsalted butter
- A dash of salt

INSTRUCTIONS:

1. Mash the banana; mix it with the almond flour, cinnamon, brown sugar, cream of tartar, vanilla, butter, and salt until consistent.
2. Microwave the mixture for 20 seconds, stir, and repeat until dough-like (2-4 times).
3. Let cool; serve at room temperature.

CHOCOLATE HAZELNUT SPREAD MOUSSE

TOTAL TIME: 15 minutes	CALORIES: 620	SERVINGS: 1	CARBS: 51	PROTEIN: 8g	FATS: 44g

INGREDIENTS:

- 1/4 jar chocolate hazelnut spread
- 2 tablespoons heavy cream
- 1/2 medium avocado
- 1/4 teaspoon vanilla extract
- A pinch of salt

INSTRUCTIONS:

1. Blend the chocolate hazelnut spread, heavy cream, avocado, vanilla extract, and salt until smooth.
2. Whip the mixture until fluffy.
3. Chill for 10 minutes.

LEMON CURD MOUSSE

TOTAL TIME: 20 minutes	CALORIES: 763	SERVINGS: 1	CARBS: 80g	PROTEIN: 10g	FATS: 47g

INGREDIENTS:

- 1/2 jar lemon curd
- 1/4 block cream cheese
- 2 tablespoons Greek yogurt
- 1 teaspoon lemon zest
- 2 tablespoons whipped cream

INSTRUCTIONS:

1. Whisk the lemon curd and cream cheese until well combined.
2. Stir in the Greek yogurt and lemon zest; blend thoroughly.
3. Fold in the whipped cream.
4. Refrigerate for 15 minutes; serve chilled.

PINEAPPLE TAPIOCA PUDDING

TOTAL TIME: 20 minutes	CALORIES: 603	SERVINGS: 1	CARBS: 69g	PROTEIN: 4g	FATS: 36g

INGREDIENTS:

- 1/4 fresh pineapple
- 2 tablespoons instant tapioca pearls
- 1/2 cup coconut milk
- 1 tablespoon honey
- 1/2 teaspoon vanilla extract
- A pinch of salt

INSTRUCTIONS:

1. Purée the pineapple until smooth.
2. Soak the tapioca pearls in warm water for 5 minutes; drain.
3. Combine the pineapple, tapioca, coconut milk, honey, vanilla, and salt in a pot; cook the mixture over medium heat; stir constantly for 10 minutes.
4. Chill for 10 minutes; serve cold.

BERRIES WITH VANILLA CUSTARD

TOTAL TIME: 30 minutes	CALORIES: 454	SERVINGS: 1	CARBS: 31g	PROTEIN: 10g	FATS: 33g

INGREDIENTS:

- 6 large strawberries
- 1/4 packet of raspberries
- 2 egg yolks
- 1 tablespoon sugar
- 1/2 teaspoon vanilla extract
- 1/4 cup milk
- 1/4 cup heavy cream

INSTRUCTIONS:

1. Purée the strawberries and raspberries until smooth.
2. Whisk the egg yolks and sugar; blend until pale.
3. Heat the milk and heavy cream in a saucepan; do not boil; gradually add the milk mixture to the egg mixture; combine.
4. Return to the saucepan; cook over low heat until thickened, stirring constantly for 10 minutes; remove from heat; add the vanilla extract.
5. Cool to room temperature; mix with the berry purée; chill for 10 minutes; serve cold.

SAFFRON MANGO MÉLANGE

TOTAL TIME: 20 minutes	CALORIES: 181	SERVINGS: 1	CARBS: 3g	PROTEIN: 7g	FATS: 4g

INGREDIENTS:

- 1/2 large mango
- A few strands of saffron
- 2 tablespoons Greek yogurt;
- 1 teaspoon honey
- 1/4 teaspoon cardamom powder

INSTRUCTIONS:

1. Infuse the saffron in 1 tablespoon of warm water; let stand for 5 minutes.
2. Purée the mango until smooth.
3. Combine the mango purée, saffron infusion, Greek yogurt, honey, and cardamom; whisk thoroughly.
4. Refrigerate for 10 minutes; serve chilled.

CHAPTER 6:
IDDSI LEVEL 4 RECIPES
(PUREED)

MAPLE-CINNAMON SWEET POTATO PURÉE

TOTAL TIME: 30 minutes	CALORIES: 232	SERVINGS: 1	CARBS: 49g	PROTEIN: 5g	FATS: 2g

INGREDIENTS:

- 1 medium sweet potato
- 1 tablespoon maple syrup
- 1/2 teaspoon cinnamon
- 1 tablespoon unsalted butter
- 1/4 teaspoon salt
- 2 tablespoons milk
- 2 tablespoons water

INSTRUCTIONS:

1. Pierce the sweet potato with a fork; microwave for 8 minutes; scoop out the inside of the sweet potato into a blender; add maple syrup, cinnamon, butter, salt, milk, and water.
2. Blend until completely smooth, add more water if too thick.
3. Serve warm, ensuring it's not too sticky or firm.

HONEYED PEAR AND COTTAGE CHEESE CREAM

TOTAL TIME: 30 minutes	CALORIES: 394	SERVINGS: 1	CARBS: 76g	PROTEIN: 14g	FATS: 7g

INGREDIENTS:

- 2 medium pears
- 1/2 cup cottage cheese
- 1 tablespoon honey
- 1/4 teaspoon ground ginger
- 1/4 teaspoon ground cinnamon
- 2 tablespoons milk

INSTRUCTIONS:

1. Peel pears, remove cores, and chop into chunks; place pears in a saucepan with a splash of water; cover and cook over medium heat for 15 minutes.
2. In a blender, combine the cooked pears, cottage cheese, honey, ginger, cinnamon, and milk.
3. Blend until the mixture is completely smooth with no lumps, adding more milk or water if necessary for a creamy consistency.

AVOCADO AND LIME BREAKFAST MOUSSE

TOTAL TIME: 10 minutes	CALORIES: 535	SERVINGS: 1	CARBS: 50g	PROTEIN: 25g	FATS: 30g

INGREDIENTS:

- 1 large avocado
- 1/2 lime
- 1 tablespoon honey
- 1/4 teaspoon vanilla extract
- 2 tablespoons Greek yogurt
- 1/2 ripe banana
- Pinch of salt

INSTRUCTIONS:

1. Peel and pit the avocado; scoop out the flesh; place the avocado, banana, lime juice, honey, vanilla extract, Greek yogurt, and salt in a blender.
2. Blend until completely smooth with no lumps.
3. Serve immediately or chill for up to 30 minutes.

COCONUT MILLET WITH PUREED STRAWBERRIES

TOTAL TIME: 30 minutes	CALORIES: 951	SERVINGS: 1	CARBS: 75g	PROTEIN: 13g	FATS: 71g

INGREDIENTS:

- 50g millet
- 1 large strawberry
- 1/4 medium coconut
- 3/4 cup coconut milk
- 1 teaspoon almond extract
- 1 tablespoon maple syrup
- Pinch of ground ginger
- Pinch of salt

INSTRUCTIONS:

1. Rinse the millet; add to the pot with coconut milk, almond extract, maple syrup, ginger, and salt; bring to a boil.
2. Simmer the millet for 20 minutes; remove from heat.
3. Hull and purée the strawberry; grate the coconut flesh.
4. Combine the cooked millet, strawberry purée, and coconut; blend until smooth.
5. Serve warm; drizzle with maple syrup.

CREAMY BANANA AND PEANUT BUTTER OATMEAL

TOTAL TIME: 20 minutes	CALORIES: 814	SERVINGS: 1	CARBS: 86g	PROTEIN: 30g	FATS: 42g

INGREDIENTS:

- 1 banana
- 2 tablespoons peanut butter
- 50g rolled oats
- 250ml milk
- 1/4 teaspoon cinnamon
- 1 teaspoon honey
- Pinch of salt

INSTRUCTIONS:

1. Blend oats to a fine powder; combine oat powder, milk, and a pinch of salt in a pot; cook until thickened.
2. Add peanut butter and cinnamon; stir until smooth.
3. Mash a banana; mix into the oatmeal until fully incorporated.
4. Drizzle honey before serving.

LEMON RICOTTA PANCAKE PURÉE

TOTAL TIME: 30 minutes	CALORIES: 593	SERVINGS: 1	CARBS: 62g	PROTEIN: 31g	FATS: 25g

INGREDIENTS:

- 1 lemon
- 100g ricotta cheese
- 2 eggs
- 1 tablespoon sugar
- 50g all-purpose flour
- 1/4 teaspoon baking powder
- Pinch of salt
- 3 tablespoons whole milk

INSTRUCTIONS:

1. Whisk the eggs, lemon zest, lemon juice, sugar, and salt; blend in the ricotta until smooth; add the flour and the baking powder; blend until a smooth batter forms.
2. Cook for 1 minute on each side; check that the pancake is cooked through but still pale and not yet browning.
3. Purée the pancakes with the milk in a blender; adjust the consistency with additional milk if needed.

SAVORY TOMATO BASIL OMELETTE PURÉE

TOTAL TIME: 30 minutes	CALORIES: 498	SERVINGS: 1	CARBS: 15g	PROTEIN: 22g	FATS: 40g

INGREDIENTS:

- 1 medium tomato
- 2 large eggs
- 6 basil leaves
- 1 tablespoon olive oil
- 1/4 small onion
- 1 garlic clove
- Salt and pepper to taste
- 1/4 teaspoon oregano
- 2 tablespoons heavy cream

INSTRUCTIONS:

1. Peel and chop the tomato and the basil leaves; mince the garlic; dice the onion.
2. Beat the eggs; mix in the heavy cream, salt, pepper, and oregano.
3. Sauté the onion and garlic in the olive oil until translucent; pour in the egg mixture; cook on low heat until set.
4. Add the tomatoes and basil to the omelet; fold gently; cook until soft.
5. Transfer the omelet to the blender; blend until smooth.

CREAMED SPINACH AND PUREED POTATO BOWL

TOTAL TIME: 30 minutes	CALORIES: 479	SERVINGS: 1	CARBS: 69g	PROTEIN: 11g	FATS: 19g

INGREDIENTS:

- 1 large potato
- 1 handful of spinach
- 1 tablespoon butter
- 1 tablespoon heavy cream
- 1/4 small onion
- 1 clove garlic
- Salt and pepper to taste
- 1 tablespoon grated Parmesan cheese

INSTRUCTIONS:

1. Peel and cube the potato; boil in water for 15 minutes; drain.
2. Sauté the chopped onion and minced garlic in the butter until translucent.
3. Add the spinach to the onion and garlic; wilt the spinach, 2 minutes.
4. Mash the potato with the heavy cream, salt, and pepper until smooth.
5. Combine the mashed potato, spinach mixture, and Parmesan; blend until puréed.

VANILLA AND MAPLE OATMEAL PUREE

TOTAL TIME: 30 minutes	CALORIES: 391	SERVINGS: 1	CARBS: 62g	PROTEIN: 14g	FATS: 10g

INGREDIENTS:

- 1/2 cup rolled oats
- 1 large egg
- 1/2 teaspoon vanilla extract
- 1 tablespoon maple syrup
- 1 teaspoon brown sugar
- 1 pinch cinnamon
- 1/2 ripe banana
- 1 cup water
- 1/4 cup whole milk

INSTRUCTIONS:

1. Grind the oats to a fine powder; beat the egg; slice the banana.
2. Boil the water, add the oats; stir continuously until thickened, 5 minutes.
3. Incorporate the milk, vanilla extract, maple syrup, brown sugar, and cinnamon; stir until evenly mixed.
4. Blend the egg into the oatmeal while hot; add the banana; blend until a smooth purée.

BUTTERNUT SQUASH AND APPLE PUREE

TOTAL TIME: 30 minutes	CALORIES: 360	SERVINGS: 1	CARBS: 68g	PROTEIN: 3g	FATS: 12g

INGREDIENTS:

- 1 small butternut squash
- 1 large apple
- 1 teaspoon cinnamon
- 1 tablespoon brown sugar
- 1/2 teaspoon ginger
- 1 tablespoon unsalted butter
- 1/4 teaspoon salt

INSTRUCTIONS:

1. Peel, seed, and cube the squash; core and cube the apple.
2. Steam the squash and apple for 20 minutes; drain.
3. Melt the butter; add the cinnamon, sugar, ginger, and salt; mix.
4. Combine the squash, apple, and spice mixture; blend until a smooth purée.
5. Serve warm; garnish with a dash of cinnamon.

PUREED MANGO COCONUT RICE PUDDING

TOTAL TIME: 30 minutes	CALORIES: 569	SERVINGS: 1	CARBS: 55g	PROTEIN: 6g	FATS: 40g

INGREDIENTS:

- 1/2 medium mango
- 1/8 medium coconut
- 25g Arborio rice
- 1/4 teaspoon vanilla extract
- 1/2 tablespoon honey
- Pinch of ground cardamom
- 1/2 cup coconut milk
- 1/2 teaspoon lime zest
- Pinch of salt

INSTRUCTIONS:

1. Peel, pit, and purée the mango; grate the coconut flesh.
2. Combine the rice, coconut milk, vanilla extract, honey, cardamom, and salt in a pot; bring to a simmer.
3. Cook the rice mixture over low heat, stirring often, for 20 minutes.
4. Remove from heat; blend the rice mixture, mango purée, and coconut until completely smooth; stir in the lime zest.
5. Serve warm or chilled; garnish with a pinch of ground cardamom.

PEACHES AND CREAM PUREED MILLET

TOTAL TIME: 30 minutes	CALORIES: 772	SERVINGS: 1	CARBS: 88g	PROTEIN: 17g	FATS: 42g

INGREDIENTS:

- 1 large peach
- 50g millet
- 1/4 medium coconut
- 3/4 cup whole milk
- 1 teaspoon honey
- Pinch of cinnamon
- Pinch of salt

INSTRUCTIONS:

1. Peel, pit, and purée the peach; grate the coconut flesh.
2. Rinse the millet; add to the pot with milk, honey, cinnamon, and salt; bring to a boil; reduce heat, simmer the millet for 15 minutes.
3. Blend the cooked millet, peach purée, and coconut until smooth.
4. Serve warm; sprinkle with cinnamon.

SMOOTH ROASTED EGGPLANT WITH TAHINI AND TOFU PUREE

TOTAL TIME: 30 minutes	CALORIES: 318	SERVINGS: 1	CARBS: 18g	PROTEIN: 10g	FATS: 26g

INGREDIENTS:

- 1/2 large eggplant
- 100g silken tofu
- 1 tablespoon tahini
- 1/2 clove garlic
- 1/2 lemon
- 1 tablespoon olive oil
- Salt to taste
- 1/8 teaspoon ground cumin
- 1/8 teaspoon paprika

INSTRUCTIONS:

1. Preheat the oven to 425°F; slice the eggplant in half lengthwise, brush with olive oil, place on a baking sheet cut-side down, roast for 25 minutes.
2. Scoop roasted eggplant into a blender; add silken tofu, tahini, garlic, lemon juice, cumin, paprika, and salt; blend until smooth.

RICH AVOCADO, CRAB AND CUCUMBER GAZPACHO PUREE

TOTAL TIME: 20 minutes	CALORIES: 863	SERVINGS: 1	CARBS: 45g	PROTEIN: 37g	FATS: 64g

INGREDIENTS:

- 1 large avocado
- 100g precooked crab meat
- 1 large cucumber
- 1 small red bell pepper
- 2 tablespoons olive oil
- 1 tablespoon lemon juice
- 1 small garlic clove
- 200ml vegetable stock
- Salt and pepper to taste
- 1 tablespoon cream
- 2 tablespoons Greek yogurt

INSTRUCTIONS:

1. Peel and pit the avocado, place in a blender; blend until smooth; add cucumber, red bell pepper, crab meat, olive oil, lemon juice, garlic to blender; blend until pureed.
2. Pour in vegetable stock gradually; season with salt and pepper; add cream and Greek yogurt; blend.
3. Chill in the refrigerator for 10 minutes; serve cold.

THICK PUREED ROASTED RED PEPPER, FETA AND CHICKPEAS

TOTAL TIME: 30 minutes	CALORIES: 449	SERVINGS: 1	CARBS: 28g	PROTEIN: 16g	FATS: 32g

INGREDIENTS:

- 1 medium red bell pepper
- 1/2 medium onion
- 1 clove garlic
- 50g canned chickpeas
- 1/2 cup feta cheese, crumbled
- 1 tablespoon olive oil
- 1/2 teaspoon smoked paprika
- 1/2 teaspoon cumin
- Salt and black pepper to taste
- 1/2 cup vegetable broth

INSTRUCTIONS:

1. Preheat the oven to 400°F; place whole bell peppers and peeled onion quarters on a baking sheet; drizzle with 1 tablespoon olive oil, sprinkle salt and pepper; roast for 20 minutes.
2. In a pan, heat remaining olive oil; sauté minced garlic for 1 minute; add roasted peppers, onion, cumin, and smoked paprika to the pan; cook for 2 minutes.
3. Combine vegetable mixture, chickpeas, feta, and vegetable broth in a blender; blend until smooth.
4. Return puree to pan; warm over low heat until heated through, stir frequently, about 5 minutes; serve warm.

LEMON-GARLIC INFUSED TUNA WITH ASPARAGUS AND BROCCOLI PUREE

TOTAL TIME: 30 minutes	CALORIES: 524	SERVINGS: 1	CARBS: 20g	PROTEIN: 49g	FATS: 35g

INGREDIENTS:

- 1 medium tuna steak
- 6 medium asparagus stalks
- 1 medium broccoli
- 2 tablespoons olive oil
- 2 cloves garlic
- 1 lemon
- Salt and pepper to taste
- 1/4 cup chicken or vegetable broth
- 1 tablespoon capers
- 1/2 teaspoon turmeric

INSTRUCTIONS:

1. Steam broccoli and asparagus for 15 minutes.
2. Poach tuna in water with lemon juice and zest, minced garlic, salt, and pepper for 10 minutes.
3. Blend vegetables with olive oil and broth.
4. Flake the cooked tuna with a fork, add capers and turmeric; blend again to a smooth consistency.

CARROT AND GINGER SOUP WITH PUREED CHICKEN

TOTAL TIME: 30 minutes	CALORIES: 726	SERVINGS: 1	CARBS: 62g	PROTEIN: 38g	FATS: 37g

INGREDIENTS:

- 1 large chicken breast
- 4 large carrots
- 1 tablespoon fresh ginger
- 2 tablespoons olive oil
- 1/2 medium onion
- 2 cloves garlic
- Salt and pepper to taste
- 1/4 teaspoon turmeric
- 500ml chicken broth
- 1 tablespoon heavy cream

INSTRUCTIONS:

1. Poach chicken breast in broth with salt and pepper for 20 minutes.
2. Sauté onion, garlic, and ginger in olive oil for 5 minutes; add chopped carrots to the mix; cover with remaining broth and simmer for 15 minutes.
3. Remove chicken and let cool slightly, then shred finely with forks.
4. Blend carrot mixture until completely smooth; combine pureed carrot mixture with shredded chicken; blend again to a uniform consistency.
5. Reheat gently, adding turmeric and cream; stir well.

HERBED PUREED ZUCCHINI WITH GRATED HALLOUMI

TOTAL TIME: 30 minutes	CALORIES: 371	SERVINGS: 1	CARBS: 17g	PROTEIN: 15g	FATS: 28g

INGREDIENTS:

- 2 medium zucchinis
- 1/2 small onion
- 1 tablespoon olive oil
- 50 grams halloumi cheese
- 1/8 teaspoon dried oregano
- 1/8 teaspoon dried basil
- Salt and pepper to taste
- 1/4 teaspoon garlic powder
- 250 ml vegetable broth

INSTRUCTIONS:

1. Sauté onion in olive oil for 3 minutes; chop zucchinis and add to the pan; sauté for an additional 2 minutes; pour vegetable broth over the zucchini and onions; simmer for 20 minutes.
2. Grate halloumi cheese.
3. Remove zucchini from heat; add oregano, basil and garlic powder.
4. Puree zucchini mixture until smooth; stir grated halloumi into the zucchini puree; blend again for a smooth consistency; serve warm.

SILKY CAULIFLOWER, LENTILS AND TAHINI PUREE

TOTAL TIME: 30 minutes	CALORIES: 494	SERVINGS: 1	CARBS: 53g	PROTEIN: 22g	FATS: 23g

INGREDIENTS:

- 1/2 medium cauliflower
- 50 grams red lentils
- 1 tablespoon tahini
- 1 tablespoon olive oil
- 1/4 medium onion
- 1 clove garlic
- Salt and pepper to taste
- 1/4 teaspoon ground cumin
- 250ml vegetable broth
- 1/2 teaspoon paprika

INSTRUCTIONS:

1. Rinse lentils; bring to a boil in vegetable broth for 15 minutes.
2. Chop cauliflower into florets; steam for 15 minutes.
3. Sauté onion and garlic in olive oil for 5 minutes.
4. Combine steamed cauliflower, cooked lentils, sautéed onion and garlic, tahini, salt, pepper, and ground cumin in a blender; puree until silky smooth, adding broth as needed to reach desired consistency; garnish with paprika.

CREAMY CELERY ROOT, WHITE BEANS AND APPLE SOUP

TOTAL TIME: 30 minutes	CALORIES: 346	SERVINGS: 1	CARBS: 39g	PROTEIN: 7g	FATS: 19g

INGREDIENTS:

- 1/2 medium celery root
- 1/2 large apple
- 100 grams canned white beans, drained and rinsed
- 1 tablespoon heavy cream
- 1/2 tablespoon unsalted butter
- 1/4 medium onion
- 1/2 clove garlic
- Salt and pepper to taste
- 1/4 teaspoon dried thyme
- 250ml vegetable broth
- 1/2 tablespoon olive oil

INSTRUCTIONS:

1. Melt butter in a pan; sauté onion and garlic for 3 minutes; add chopped celery root and apple to the pan; sauté for 2 minutes; pour in vegetable broth; simmer for 20 minutes; add white beans to the pot in the last 5 minutes of cooking.
2. Blend the mixture with heavy cream until smooth.
3. Stir in olive oil, thyme, salt and pepper.

SMOOTH POLENTA WITH SUN DRIED TOMATOES AND RICOTTA CHEESE

TOTAL TIME: 30 minutes	CALORIES: 707	SERVINGS: 1	CARBS: 63g	PROTEIN: 20g	FATS: 44g

INGREDIENTS:

- 50g instant polenta
- 4 sun-dried tomatoes
- 100g ricotta cheese
- 2 tablespoons Parmesan cheese
- 1 tablespoon olive oil
- 1 clove garlic
- Salt and pepper to taste
- 1/2 teaspoon dried basil
- 500ml water or chicken broth
- 1 tablespoon butter
- 1/2 teaspoon dried oregano

INSTRUCTIONS:

1. Bring water or broth to a boil; whisk in polenta gradually for 5 minutes; reduce heat to low; add olive oil, minced garlic, sun-dried tomatoes, basil, and oregano; simmer gently, stirring frequently, for 5 minutes; stir in ricotta and Parmesan cheeses until well incorporated.
2. Season with salt and black pepper; add butter.
3. Blend to achieve a smooth consistency; serve warm.

PUREED SPICY TOMATO AND RED LENTIL SOUP

TOTAL TIME: 30 minutes	CALORIES: 519	SERVINGS: 1	CARBS: 74g	PROTEIN: 21g	FATS: 17g

INGREDIENTS:

- 75g red lentils
- 1/2 large tomato
- 1/2 small carrot
- 1/2 small potato
- 1/2 small onion
- 1 clove garlic
- 1 tablespoon olive oil
- 375ml vegetable broth
- 1/4 teaspoon smoked paprika
- Salt to taste
- 1/2 tablespoon tomato paste

INSTRUCTIONS:

1. Heat olive oil in a pot; sauté onion and garlic for 3 minutes; add chopped and peeled tomato, carrot, potato, and cook for another 2 minutes; stir in tomato paste, smoked paprika, and salt.
2. Add red lentils and vegetable broth; bring to a boil, then simmer for 20 minutes.
3. Blend the soup until smooth, adding more broth if necessary for the right consistency; serve warm.

RICH TURKEY AND SWEET POTATO BLEND

TOTAL TIME: 30 minutes	CALORIES: 817	SERVINGS: 1	CARBS: 46g	PROTEIN: 40g	FATS: 54g

INGREDIENTS:

- 200g ground turkey
- 1 large sweet potato
- 2 tablespoons olive oil
- 1/2 medium onion
- 1 clove garlic
- Salt and pepper to taste
- 1/4 teaspoon ground cinnamon
- 500ml chicken broth
- 1 tablespoon unsalted butter

INSTRUCTIONS:

1. Sauté onion and garlic in olive oil for 3 minutes; add ground turkey; cook for 5 minutes.
2. Combine peeled and chopped sweet potato and broth in a pot; bring to boil and cook for 15 minutes; drain sweet potatoes, reserving broth.
3. Blend sweet potatoes with turkey, adding reserved broth as needed to reach desired consistency; add cinnamon and butter; blend until smooth.
4. Season with salt and pepper; serve warm.

SAVORY BEEF AND MUSHROOM PURÉE

TOTAL TIME: 30 minutes	CALORIES: 815	SERVINGS: 1	CARBS: 6g	PROTEIN: 45g	FATS: 69g

INGREDIENTS:

- 200g ground beef
- 1 cup Portobello mushrooms
- 2 tablespoons olive oil
- 1/4 medium onion
- 1 clove garlic
- Salt and pepper to taste
- 1/4 teaspoon dried thyme
- 500ml beef broth
- 1 tablespoon cream
- 1 teaspoon Worcestershire sauce

INSTRUCTIONS:

1. Heat olive oil in a pan; sauté onion and garlic for 3 minutes; add ground beef; cook for 5 minutes; add chopped mushrooms; cook for 5 minutes; pour in beef broth; simmer for 10 minutes.
2. Transfer beef and mushroom mixture to a blender, adding thyme, cream, and Worcestershire sauce; blend until completely smooth, adding broth as needed to adjust consistency.
3. Reheat the purée gently, season with salt and pepper; serve warm.

GARLIC BUTTER SOLE PUREE AND APPLE GLAZED CARROT

TOTAL TIME: 30 minutes	CALORIES: 898	SERVINGS: 1	CARBS: 55g	PROTEIN: 26g	FATS: 65g

INGREDIENTS:

- 200g sole filet
- 3 medium carrots
- 1 medium apple
- 2 tablespoons unsalted butter
- 1 clove garlic
- 2 tablespoons olive oil
- Salt and pepper to taste
- 1 teaspoon apple cider vinegar
- 1 tablespoon honey
- 2 tablespoons heavy cream

INSTRUCTIONS:

1. Steam the peeled and chopped carrots and apple for 15 minutes.
2. In a small pan, melt 1 tablespoon butter; add apple cider vinegar and honey; stir to create a glaze; blend steamed carrots and apple with the glaze until smooth.
3. In a separate pan, heat 1 tablespoon olive oil; add minced garlic and sauté until fragrant; add sole filet and cook for 6 minutes per side, seasoning with salt and pepper.
4. Flake the cooked sole and blend with 1 tablespoon of butter and heavy cream until smooth.

SPICED PUMPKIN AND CHICKEN CREAM

TOTAL TIME: 30 minutes	CALORIES: 622	SERVINGS: 1	CARBS: 9g	PROTEIN: 46g	FATS: 41g

INGREDIENTS:

- 200 grams chicken breast
- 1/4 of a medium pumpkin
- 2 tablespoons olive oil
- 1 small onion
- 1 clove garlic
- Salt and pepper to taste
- 1/2 teaspoon ground cinnamon
- 500ml chicken broth
- 2 tablespoons cream cheese

INSTRUCTIONS:

1. Poach chicken breast in chicken broth for 15 minutes.
2. Sauté onion and garlic in olive oil for 5 minutes; add peeled and chopped pumpkin to the onion and garlic, cover with the remaining broth, and simmer for 15 minutes.
3. Shred the chicken; blend pumpkin mixture until smooth; combine shredded chicken with the pumpkin puree, add cream cheese.
4. Season with cinnamon, salt, and pepper.

GARLIC THYME BEEF PUREE WITH ASPARAGUS AND POTATO CREAM

TOTAL TIME: 30 minutes	CALORIES: 969	SERVINGS: 1	CARBS: 35	PROTEIN: 48	FATS: 73

INGREDIENTS:

- 200g ground beef
- 1 medium potato
- 5 asparagus spears
- 2 tablespoons olive oil
- 1 clove garlic
- 1 teaspoon dried thyme
- Salt and pepper to taste
- 500ml beef broth
- 1 tablespoon cream
- 1 teaspoon butter

INSTRUCTIONS:

1. Cook ground beef in a pan with minced garlic, dried thyme, salt, and pepper for 10 minutes.
2. Steam the peeled and chopped potato and asparagus for 15 minutes.
3. Puree cooked beef with butter, adding a little beef broth.
4. Blend steamed potato with asparagus and cream, season with salt and pepper, adding broth as needed.

PUREED LEMON HERB SALMON WITH ROASTED CAULIFLOWER

TOTAL TIME: 30 minutes	CALORIES: 794	SERVINGS: 1	CARBS: 19g	PROTEIN: 44g	FATS: 56g

INGREDIENTS:

- 200g salmon filet
- 1/4 large cauliflower
- 2 tablespoons olive oil
- 1 lemon
- 1 teaspoon dried dill
- Salt and pepper to taste
- 1 tablespoon butter
- 1 teaspoon capers

INSTRUCTIONS:

1. Preheat the oven to 390°F; toss cauliflower florets with 1 tablespoon olive oil, salt, and pepper; roast for 20 minutes.
2. Season salmon with lemon zest, dried dill, salt, and pepper.
3. Heat remaining olive oil in a pan, add salmon; cook for 7 minutes per side, adding lemon juice halfway through; puree the salmon in a blender with butter.
4. Blend roasted cauliflower until creamy, adding broth if necessary.

CREAMY ROSEMARY LAMB PURÉE WITH BEET AND MINT

TOTAL TIME: 30 minutes	CALORIES: 807	SERVINGS: 1	CARBS: 15g	PROTEIN: 47g	FATS: 65g

INGREDIENTS:

- 200g lamb shoulder
- 1 large beet
- 2 tablespoons olive oil
- 1 teaspoon fresh rosemary
- Salt and pepper to taste
- 1/2 teaspoon balsamic vinegar
- 1 teaspoon fresh mint
- 1 tablespoon Greek yogurt

INSTRUCTIONS:

1. Brown trimmed lamb cubes in 1 tablespoon olive oil with rosemary, salt, and pepper; cover with water, simmer for 20 minutes.
2. Roast peeled and chopped beet in a preheated oven at 390°F with remaining olive oil and a pinch of salt for 20 minutes.
3. Purée cooked lamb with cooking liquid until smooth.
4. Blend roasted beet with balsamic vinegar, fresh mint, and Greek yogurt.

ZESTY ORANGE GLAZED TURKEY PURÉE WITH HERBED WHITE BEAN

TOTAL TIME: 30 minutes	CALORIES: 662	SERVINGS: 1	CARBS: 37g	PROTEIN: 37g	FATS: 41g

INGREDIENTS:

- 200g turkey breast
- 100g canned white beans
- 1 orange
- 2 tablespoons olive oil
- 1 teaspoon dried thyme
- Salt and pepper to taste
- 1 tablespoon unsalted butter

INSTRUCTIONS:

1. Poach turkey breast in water with half the orange juice and zest, salt, and pepper for 15 minutes; in the same pot, add drained and rinsed white beans during the last 5 minutes of cooking.
2. Reserve some of the cooking liquid; heat 1 tablespoon olive oil in a pan, add cooked turkey and beans, sauté with dried herbs and remaining orange zest for 3 minutes to enhance flavor development.
3. Transfer the mixture to a blender, add remaining orange juice and butter, and blend until smooth, adding reserved cooking liquid as needed.

COD CREAM AND BUTTERY PUREED PARSNIP AND LEEK

TOTAL TIME: 30 minutes	CALORIES: 950	SERVINGS: 1	CARBS: 60g	PROTEIN: 44g	FATS: 57g

INGREDIENTS:

- 200g cod filet
- 2 medium parsnips
- 1 leek
- 2 tablespoons unsalted butter
- 2 tablespoons olive oil
- Salt and pepper to taste
- 500ml vegetable broth
- 1 tablespoon cream

INSTRUCTIONS:

1. Poach cod in a portion of the vegetable broth for 10 minutes.
2. Sauté the chopped white parts of the leek in olive oil for 5 minutes; add peeled and chopped parsnips to leeks, cover with remaining broth, and simmer for 15 minutes.
3. Drain cod and vegetables, reserving the broth; blend cod, parsnips, leeks, and butter in a blender, adding reserved broth as needed to achieve a smooth consistency; stir in cream; season with salt and pepper.

BEETROOT, TOFU AND YOGURT SOUP

TOTAL TIME: 30 minutes	CALORIES: 592	SERVINGS: 1	CARBS: 39g	PROTEIN: 35g	FATS: 35g

INGREDIENTS:

- 2 large beetroots
- 200g firm tofu
- 1 tablespoon olive oil
- 500ml vegetable broth
- 100g plain Greek yogurt
- Salt and pepper to taste
- 1/2 teaspoon ground cumin
- 1 tablespoon tahini

INSTRUCTIONS:

1. In a pot, sauté peeled and chopped beetroots in olive oil for 5 minutes; add vegetable broth and bring to a boil; reduce heat and simmer for 20 minutes; add tofu cubes in the last 5 minutes of cooking.
2. Blend beetroot, tofu, and broth until completely smooth; stir in Greek yogurt and tahini; season with cumin, salt, and pepper.

QUAIL EGG AND TURKEY MEDALLIONS WITH ROASTED BELL PEPPERS

TOTAL TIME: 30 minutes	CALORIES: 656	SERVINGS: 1	CARBS: 12g	PROTEIN: 46g	FATS: 47g

INGREDIENTS:

- 200g turkey breast
- 6 quail eggs
- 2 large red and yellow bell peppers
- 2 tablespoons olive oil
- Salt and pepper to taste
- 1 teaspoon smoked paprika
- 1 tablespoon cream

INSTRUCTIONS:

1. Roast chopped bell peppers with 1 tablespoon olive oil and a pinch of salt at 390°F for 15 minutes.
2. Hard boil quail eggs, cool them quickly under cold water, and peel.
3. Sauté small turkey pieces in 1 tablespoon olive oil for 10 minutes.
4. Puree roasted bell peppers, season with salt and smoked paprika.
5. Blend quail eggs separately.
6. Puree cooked turkey, adding cream, salt, and pepper.

SEA BASS AND ARTICHOKE HEART PUREE

TOTAL TIME: 30 minutes	CALORIES: 505	SERVINGS: 1	CARBS: 18g	PROTEIN: 29g	FATS: 38g

INGREDIENTS:

- 200g sea bass filet
- 150g canned artichoke hearts
- 2 tablespoons olive oil
- 1 small onion
- 1 clove garlic
- Salt and pepper to taste
- 1 tablespoon cream
- 1 teaspoon lemon zest

INSTRUCTIONS:

1. Sauté onion and garlic in 1 tablespoon olive oil for 3 minutes; add sea bass filet to the pan, season with salt and pepper, cook for 7 minutes per side.
2. In a blender, combine cooked sea bass, drained artichoke hearts, remaining olive oil, and lemon zest; puree until smooth, add cream.

CINNAMON ROLL APPLE PUREE

TOTAL TIME: 30 minutes	CALORIES: 475	SERVINGS: 1	CARBS: 83g	PROTEIN: 3g	FATS: 17g

INGREDIENTS:

- 2 medium apples
- 1 tablespoon unsalted butter
- 1/2 teaspoon ground cinnamon
- 1 tablespoon brown sugar
- 1/4 teaspoon vanilla extract
- 1 tablespoon maple syrup
- 2 tablespoons whole milk
- 1 tablespoon cream cheese

INSTRUCTIONS:

1. Chop the peeled and cored apples into chunks; steam for 15 minutes.
2. In a pan, melt butter; add steamed apples, cinnamon, brown sugar, and vanilla; cook for 5 minutes.
3. Transfer to a blender; add maple syrup and milk; blend until completely smooth.
4. Pass through a sieve to ensure no lumps; return to the pan, add cream cheese; stir until melted and well combine; serve warm.

CREAMY MUSHROOM AND THYME SOUP

TOTAL TIME: 30 minutes	CALORIES: 495	SERVINGS: 1	CARBS: 23g	PROTEIN: 4g	FATS: 43g

INGREDIENTS:

- 8 medium button mushrooms
- 1 small onion
- 1 clove garlic
- 2 tablespoons olive oil
- 1 teaspoon fresh thyme leaves
- 1/2 teaspoon ground black pepper
- 1/2 teaspoon salt
- 1 tablespoon cornstarch
- 2 tablespoons water
- 250ml vegetable stock
- 3 tablespoons heavy cream

INSTRUCTIONS:

1. Clean mushrooms; chop mushrooms and onion finely; mince garlic.
2. Heat olive oil in a pot; add mushrooms, onion, garlic, thyme; sauté for 10 minutes.
3. Dissolve cornstarch in water; add to pot with vegetable stock; bring to boil.
4. Simmer for 10 minutes; remove from heat; blend until smooth with immersion blender.
5. Return to pot; add cream; heat for 5 minutes without boiling.

CHEESY CARROT PURÉE

TOTAL TIME: 25 minutes	CALORIES: 536	SERVINGS: 1	CARBS: 50g	PROTEIN: 13g	FATS: 34g

INGREDIENTS:

- 3 medium carrots
- 1 small potato
- 2 tablespoons unsalted butter
- 1/4 cup shredded cheddar cheese
- 1/4 teaspoon garlic powder
- 1/4 teaspoon onion powder
- Salt and pepper to taste
- 1/2 cup milk

INSTRUCTIONS:

1. Chop peeled carrots and potato into small chunks; boil them in water for 15 minutes;
2. Drain water and transfer vegetables to a blender; add butter, cheddar cheese, garlic powder, onion powder, and a pinch of salt; purée mixture, gradually adding milk until the purée is smooth but not liquidy; serve warm.

MANGO TANGO COCONUT MOUSSE

TOTAL TIME: 20 minutes	CALORIES: 527	SERVINGS: 1	CARBS: 90g	PROTEIN: 4g	FATS: 20g

INGREDIENTS:

- 1 large mango
- 200ml coconut milk
- 2 tablespoons honey
- 1 teaspoon vanilla extract
- 1/4 teaspoon ground cardamom

INSTRUCTIONS:

1. Cut mango into chunks.
2. Place mango chunks, coconut milk, honey, vanilla extract, and cardamom in a blender; blend for 4 minutes.
3. Chill in the refrigerator for 15 minutes.

ROASTED GARLIC AND POTATO SILK

TOTAL TIME: 30 minutes	CALORIES: 726	SERVINGS: 1	CARBS: 62g	PROTEIN: 18g	FATS: 51g

INGREDIENTS:

- 2 medium potatoes
- 1 whole garlic
- 2 tablespoons olive oil
- 1/4 cup heavy cream
- Salt and pepper to taste
- 1 tablespoon grated Parmesan cheese

INSTRUCTIONS:

1. Preheat the oven to 400°F; cut the top off the head of garlic to expose the cloves; drizzle with 1 tablespoon olive oil and wrap in foil; bake it for 20 minutes.
2. Peel and dice potatoes; boil in salted water for 15 minutes.
3. Drain potatoes and return to the pot; squeeze the roasted garlic out of its skins and add to the potatoes; add heavy cream, remaining olive oil, Parmesan cheese, salt, and pepper.
4. Blend with an immersion blender until smooth.

SPICED LENTIL AND TOMATO CREAM

TOTAL TIME: 30 minutes	CALORIES: 586	SERVINGS: 1	CARBS: 48g	PROTEIN: 15g	FATS: 40g

INGREDIENTS:

- 50g red lentils
- 1 small tomato
- 1 small carrot
- 1/2 small onion
- 1 clove garlic
- 2 tablespoons olive oil
- 1/2 teaspoon cumin powder
- 1/2 teaspoon coriander powder
- 1/4 teaspoon paprika
- Salt and pepper to taste
- 250ml water
- 2 tablespoons heavy cream

INSTRUCTIONS:

1. Rinse lentils; peel and chop carrot and tomato; finely dice onion; mince garlic.
2. Heat olive oil in a saucepan; add onion, garlic; sauté for 3 minutes.
3. Add carrots, tomatoes, cumin, coriander, paprika; cook for 5 minutes.
4. Add lentils and water; bring to boil; simmer for 15 minutes.
5. Blend to a smooth consistency with an immersion blender; stir in heavy cream; season with salt and pepper.

BBQ SWEET POTATO WHIP

TOTAL TIME: 30 minutes	CALORIES: 591	SERVINGS: 1	CARBS: 56g	PROTEIN: 5g	FATS: 41g

INGREDIENTS:

- 1 large sweet potato
- 1 tablespoon unsalted butter
- 2 tablespoons smooth BBQ sauce
- 1/4 teaspoon smoked paprika
- Salt to taste
- 1 tablespoon olive oil
- 2 tablespoons milk

INSTRUCTIONS:

1. Peel sweet potato; cut into large chunks; boil sweet potato chunks in water for 20 minutes; drain sweet potatoes; return to pot; add butter, BBQ sauce, smoked paprika, and salt; blend with immersion blender until smooth.
2. Add olive oil and milk; whip to incorporate air and ensure smoothness.
3. Warm up for 2 minutes on low heat, stirring constantly.

CHEDDAR AND BROCCOLI SOUP PUREE

TOTAL TIME: 30 minutes	CALORIES: 683	SERVINGS: 1	CARBS: 31g	PROTEIN: 20g	FATS: 35g

INGREDIENTS:

- 1 large broccoli
- 1 small onion
- 1 clove garlic
- 1 tablespoon vegetable oil
- 30 grams cheddar cheese
- 300ml chicken broth
- Salt and pepper to taste
- 1/4 teaspoon smooth mustard
- 2 tablespoons heavy cream

INSTRUCTIONS:

1. Chop broccoli into florets; dice onion; mince garlic.
2. Heat oil in a pot; sauté onion and garlic for 3 minutes.
3. Add broccoli and broth; cover and simmer for 10 minutes.
4. Remove from heat; add cheddar cheese, mustard powder, salt, and pepper.
5. Use an immersion blender to puree the soup until smooth; stir in heavy cream; serve warm.

CREAMY AVOCADO AND LIME PUDDING

TOTAL TIME: 20 minutes	CALORIES: 453	SERVINGS: 1	CARBS: 37g	PROTEIN: 6g	FATS: 36g

INGREDIENTS:

- 1 avocado
- 1 lime
- 1 tablespoon honey
- 1 tablespoon coconut oil
- Pinch of salt
- 1/4 teaspoon vanilla extract
- 1 tablespoon plain Greek yogurt

INSTRUCTIONS:

1. Place avocado, lime juice, honey, coconut oil, salt, and vanilla extract in a blender; blend until completely smooth.
2. Add Greek yogurt; blend again to incorporate.
3. Transfer to a bowl; chill in the refrigerator if desired for 10 minutes.

GOLDEN KIWI AND BANANA FUSION

TOTAL TIME: 15 minutes	CALORIES: 304	SERVINGS: 1	CARBS: 71g	PROTEIN: 6g	FATS: 1g

INGREDIENTS:

- 2 golden kiwis
- 1 medium banana
- 1 tablespoon honey
- 2 tablespoons Greek yogurt
- Dash of cinnamon
- 1 tablespoon orange juice

INSTRUCTIONS:

1. Place kiwis, banana, honey, and orange juice in a blender; blend until completely smooth.
2. Add Greek yogurt and cinnamon; blend again until well mixed.
3. If desired, chill in the refrigerator for 10 minutes before serving.

ROASTED PLUM AND VANILLA BEAN PURÉE

TOTAL TIME: 30 minutes	CALORIES: 237	SERVINGS: 1	CARBS: 34g	PROTEIN: 4g	FATS: 11g

INGREDIENTS:

- 3 medium plums
- 1 teaspoon vanilla extract
- 1 tablespoon brown sugar
- 2 teaspoons olive oil
- Pinch of ground cinnamon
- 2 tablespoons Greek yogurt

INSTRUCTIONS:

1. Preheat the oven to 375°F.
2. Halve plums, remove pits, place on baking sheet; drizzle with olive oil; sprinkle brown sugar and cinnamon over plums; roast in the oven for 15 minutes.
3. Remove from the oven; allow plums to cool slightly; blend plums with any released juices and vanilla extract; stir in Greek yogurt until fully incorporated.

CREAMY CAJUN BUTTERNUT SQUASH

TOTAL TIME: 30 minutes	CALORIES: 329	SERVINGS: 1	CARBS: 30g	PROTEIN: 3g	FATS: 24g

INGREDIENTS:

- 1/2 medium butternut squash
- 1 tablespoon olive oil
- 1/2 teaspoon Cajun seasoning
- Salt to taste
- 1/4 teaspoon garlic powder
- 50ml cream
- 50ml vegetable broth

INSTRUCTIONS:

1. Peel squash, remove seeds, chop into small pieces.
2. Toss squash with olive oil, Cajun seasoning, garlic powder, and salt.
3. Arrange on a baking tray; roast at 425°F for 20 minutes.
4. Transfer roasted squash to a blender; add cream and vegetable broth; blend until smooth.

DESSERTS

CHOCOLATE PEANUT BUTTER SILK

TOTAL TIME: 15 minutes	CALORIES: 365	SERVINGS: 1	CARBS: 39g	PROTEIN: 15g	FATS: 20g

INGREDIENTS:

- 1 small banana
- 2 tablespoons peanut butter
- 2 tablespoons cocoa powder
- 100g silken tofu
- 1 teaspoon vanilla extract
- A pinch of salt
- 2 tablespoons heavy cream

INSTRUCTIONS:

1. Peel the banana; blend; add peanut butter, cocoa powder, silken tofu, vanilla extract, salt to blender; blend until fully smooth.
2. Refrigerate for 10 minutes to set; serve chilled.

PINA COLADA CREAM

TOTAL TIME: 10 minutes	CALORIES: 146	SERVINGS: 1	CARBS: 24g	PROTEIN: 3g	FATS: 4g

INGREDIENTS:

- 1/2 medium banana
- 1/4 cup canned pineapple
- 1 tablespoon coconut cream
- 2 tablespoons Greek yogurt
- A pinch of salt

INSTRUCTIONS:

1. Combine banana and drained pineapple in a blender; puree until smooth; add coconut cream, Greek yogurt, and salt; blend until completely smooth.
2. Refrigerate for 10 minutes to thicken; serve chilled.

CARAMEL FLAN

TOTAL TIME: 15 minutes	CALORIES: 207	SERVINGS: 1	CARBS: 21g	PROTEIN: 6g	FATS: 12g

INGREDIENTS:

- 1/2 small avocado
- 1 tablespoon caramel sauce
- 1/4 cup milk
- 1 teaspoon gelatin powder
- 1 tablespoon warm water
- 1 teaspoon vanilla extract
- A pinch of salt

INSTRUCTIONS:

1. Dissolve gelatin in warm water; let it bloom for 5 minutes; blend avocado until smooth.
2. Gently heat milk in a saucepan; do not boil; remove milk from heat; whisk in bloomed gelatin until dissolved; add caramel sauce, vanilla extract, and salt; stir well; combine milk mixture with pureed avocado; blend until homogenous.
3. Pour into a mold; refrigerate for 20 minutes to set.

TROPICAL FRUIT PUREE WITH COCONUT

TOTAL TIME: 15 minutes	CALORIES: 252	SERVINGS: 1	CARBS: 51g	PROTEIN: 3g	FATS: 6g

INGREDIENTS:

- 1/4 mango
- 1/4 ripe papaya
- 1/2 small banana
- 2 tablespoons coconut milk
- 1 tablespoon lime
- A pinch of ground cinnamon
- A drizzle of honey

INSTRUCTIONS:

1. Puree mango, papaya, and banana in a blender; add coconut milk, lime juice, cinnamon, and honey; blend until well combined.
2. Refrigerate for 5 minutes; serve chilled.

RASPBERRY AND WHITE CHOCOLATE MOUSSE

TOTAL TIME: 20 minutes	CALORIES: 392	SERVINGS: 1	CARBS: 23g	PROTEIN: 5g	FATS: 33g

INGREDIENTS:

- 1/2 cup fresh raspberries
- 1/4 cup white chocolate chips
- 1/4 cup heavy cream
- 1/2 teaspoon vanilla extract
- A pinch of salt

INSTRUCTIONS:

1. Puree raspberries in a blender until smooth; strain through a fine-mesh sieve to remove seeds.
2. Whip heavy cream with vanilla extract and salt until soft peaks form.
3. Fold in melted and cooled white chocolate into whipped cream until no streaks remain; incorporate raspberry puree into the white chocolate mixture until well combined.
4. Refrigerate for 15 minutes; serve chilled.

CARROT CAKE PUREE

TOTAL TIME: 30 minutes	CALORIES: 122	SERVINGS: 1	CARBS: 19g	PROTEIN: 2g	FATS: 5g

INGREDIENTS:

- 1 medium carrot
- 1/2 small apple
- 1 tablespoon cream cheese
- 1/4 teaspoon cinnamon
- Drop of vanilla extract
- 1 teaspoon maple syrup
- Water or unsweetened apple juice

INSTRUCTIONS:

1. Peel and core the apple and carrot; chop them into small pieces.
2. Place the carrot in a steamer basket for 15 minutes; add the apple for the last 5 minutes.
3. Transfer the carrot and apple to a blender; puree; add the cream cheese, cinnamon, maple syrup and vanilla extract; blend.
4. Refrigerate for 5 minutes; serve chilled.

ORANGE CREAMSICLE PUDDING

TOTAL TIME: 20 minutes	CALORIES: 165	SERVINGS: 1	CARBS: 29g	PROTEIN: 13g	FATS: 3g

INGREDIENTS:

- 1/2 cup Greek yogurt
- 1/4 cup orange juice
- 1/2 teaspoon vanilla extract
- 1 tablespoon honey
- 2 tablespoons whipped cream

INSTRUCTIONS:

1. In a blender, combine the Greek yogurt and orange juice; blend; add the vanilla extract and honey; blend again.
2. Refrigerate for 15 minutes; serve chilled.

LEMON BLUEBERRY VELVET

TOTAL TIME: 20 minutes	CALORIES: 447	SERVINGS: 1	CARBS: 35g	PROTEIN: 12g	FATS: 23g

INGREDIENTS:

- 1/2 cup blueberries
- 1 lemon
- 1/2 cup ricotta cheese
- 2 tablespoons honey
- 2 tablespoons heavy cream

INSTRUCTIONS:

1. Blend blueberries until completely smooth; add the lemon zest, 2 tablespoons lemon juice, ricotta cheese, heavy cream and honey to the blender; blend again.
2. Refrigerate for 15 minutes; serve chilled.

BLACK FOREST CHOCOLATE CREAM

TOTAL TIME: 25 minutes	CALORIES: 431	SERVINGS: 1	CARBS: 37g	PROTEIN: 6g	FATS: 31g

INGREDIENTS:

- 1/2 cup canned cherries
- 1/4 cup dark chocolate
- 1/4 cup heavy cream
- 1 tablespoon cocoa powder
- 2 tablespoons sugar

INSTRUCTIONS:

1. In a small saucepan, gently warm the heavy cream without boiling; stir in the cocoa powder and sugar until dissolved; add the dark chocolate, stir until smooth.
2. In a blender, puree the canned cherries until smooth; mix the cherry puree into the chocolate mixture.
3. Refrigerate for 15 minutes; serve chilled.

ESPRESSO AND COCOA PUDDING

TOTAL TIME: 20 minutes	CALORIES: 148	SERVINGS: 1	CARBS: 24g	PROTEIN: 4g	FATS: 5g

INGREDIENTS:

- 1/2 cup whole milk
- 1 teaspoon instant espresso powder
- 2 tablespoons cocoa powder
- 2 tablespoons sugar
- 1 tablespoon cornstarch
- 1/4 teaspoon vanilla extract
- A pinch of salt

INSTRUCTIONS:

1. In a small bowl, mix the cornstarch with a few tablespoons of milk.
2. In a saucepan over medium heat, combine the remaining milk, espresso powder, sifted cocoa powder, sugar, and salt. Stir until the sugar has dissolved.
3. Add the cornstarch slurry to the mixture; stir until the mixture begins to bubble gently; remove from heat and stir in the vanilla extract.
4. Allow the mixture to cool slightly, then transfer it to a blender and puree until the texture is completely smooth; refrigerate for 15 minutes; serve chilled.

BANANA COCONUT CREAM

TOTAL TIME: 20 minutes	CALORIES: 288	SERVINGS: 1	CARBS: 46g	PROTEIN: 3g	FATS: 12g

INGREDIENTS:

- 1 banana
- 1/4 cup coconut milk
- 1 tablespoon honey
- 1/2 teaspoon vanilla extract
- A pinch of cinnamon

INSTRUCTIONS:

1. In a blender, puree the banana until smooth; add the coconut milk, honey, vanilla extract, and cinnamon to the pureed banana; blend again.
2. Refrigerate for 15 minutes; serve chilled.

PEACH MELBA PUDDING

TOTAL TIME: 25 minutes	CALORIES: 359	SERVINGS: 1	CARBS: 39g	PROTEIN: 4g	FATS: 22g

INGREDIENTS:

- 1/2 cup canned peaches in syrup
- 1/4 cup raspberries
- 1/4 cup heavy cream
- 1 tablespoon sugar
- 1 teaspoon vanilla extract
- A pinch of salt

INSTRUCTIONS:

1. Blend the drained peaches and raspberries in a blender; strain the puree through a fine mesh sieve if you're concerned about the seeds.
2. Combine the pureed fruits with sugar and a pinch of salt in a small saucepan; cook over medium heat until the sugar dissolves; reduce the heat to low and stir in the heavy cream and vanilla extract; transfer the mixture back to the blender and blend again.
3. Refrigerate for 15 minutes; serve chilled.

SMOOTHIES

BLUEBERRY LAVENDER SMOOTHIE

TOTAL TIME: 10 minutes	CALORIES: 431	SERVINGS: 1	CARBS: 68g	PROTEIN: 10g	FATS: 18g

INGREDIENTS:

- 1 large banana
- 1/2 medium avocado
- 1/2 cup blueberries
- 1 tablespoon edible dried lavender
- 1 tablespoon honey
- 200ml whole milk

INSTRUCTIONS:

1. Combine banana, avocado, blueberries, lavender, honey, and whole milk in a blender.
2. Serve immediately.

MANGO AND BANANA SMOOTHIE

TOTAL TIME: 30 minutes	CALORIES: 380	SERVINGS: 1	CARBS: 78g	PROTEIN: 11g	FATS: 8g

INGREDIENTS:

- 1 large mango
- 1 large banana
- 200ml whole milk
- 1 teaspoon vanilla extract
- 1/2 teaspoon ground cinnamon
- 2 tablespoons rolled oats

INSTRUCTIONS:

1. Combine mango, banana, whole milk, vanilla extract, and ground cinnamon in a blender; add rolled oats for a thicker texture and blend until smooth.
2. Serve immediately.

KIWI AND CUCUMBER SMOOTHIE

TOTAL TIME: 10 minutes	CALORIES: 22g	SERVINGS: 1	CARBS: 34	PROTEIN: 10g	FATS: 8g

INGREDIENTS:

- 2 kiwis
- 1/2 large cucumber
- 200ml whole milk
- A few fresh mint leaves
- 1 tablespoon lime juice

INSTRUCTIONS:

1. Combine kiwis, cucumber, whole milk, lime juice and mint leaves in a blender.
2. Serve immediately.

APRICOT AND HONEY SMOOTHIE

TOTAL TIME: 10 minutes	CALORIES: 265	SERVINGS: 1	CARBS: 44g	PROTEIN: 11g	FATS: 9g

INGREDIENTS:

- 4 medium apricots
- 1 tablespoon honey
- 200ml whole milk
- 1/2 teaspoon ground cardamom
- 2 tablespoons Greek yogurt

INSTRUCTIONS:

1. Combine apricots, honey, milk, ground cardamom, and Greek yogurt in a blender.
2. Serve immediately.

PAPAYA AND COCONUT SMOOTHIE

TOTAL TIME: 10 minutes	CALORIES: 327	SERVINGS: 1	CARBS: 53g	PROTEIN: 9g	FATS: 12g

INGREDIENTS:

- 1/2 ripe papaya
- 200ml whole milk
- 1/2 cup pineapple
- 1 tablespoon coconut cream
- 1/4 teaspoon ground cinnamon
- 1 teaspoon honey

INSTRUCTIONS:

1. Scoop papaya flesh and pineapple chunks into a blender; add whole milk, ground cinnamon, honey and coconut cream; blend until completely smooth.
2. Serve immediately.

HONEYDEW MELON AND MINT SMOOTHIE

TOTAL TIME: 10 minutes	CALORIES: 244	SERVINGS: 1	CARBS: 61g	PROTEIN: 3g	FATS: 4g

INGREDIENTS:

- 1/2 large honeydew melon
- A handful of fresh mint leaves
- 200ml coconut milk
- 1 tablespoon lime juice
- 1 teaspoon honey

INSTRUCTIONS:

1. Remove seeds and scoop the flesh from the honeydew melon.
2. In a blender, combine the honeydew melon flesh, mint leaves, honey, coconut milk, and lime juice.
3. Serve chilled.

STRAWBERRY ROSE CREAM SMOOTHIE

TOTAL TIME: 10 minutes	CALORIES: 246	SERVINGS: 1	CARBS: 38g	PROTEIN: 11g	FATS: 9g

INGREDIENTS:

- 1 cup strawberries
- 200ml whole milk
- 2 tablespoons Greek yogurt
- 1 tablespoon rose water
- 1 tablespoon honey

INSTRUCTIONS:

1. Combine strawberries, milk, Greek yogurt, rose water, and honey in a blender.
2. Serve immediately.

CITRUS CREAMSICLE SMOOTHIE

TOTAL TIME: 10 minutes	CALORIES: 404	SERVINGS: 1	CARBS: 57g	PROTEIN: 18g	FATS: 13g

INGREDIENTS:

- 1 large orange
- 1/2 cup Greek yogurt
- 200ml whole milk
- 1 tablespoon vanilla extract
- 1 tablespoon honey

INSTRUCTIONS:

1. Ensure the orange is peeled with no pith remaining; section it.
2. Combine the orange sections, Greek yogurt, whole milk, vanilla extract, and honey in a blender.
3. Serve chilled.

BEET AND BERRY SMOOTHIE

TOTAL TIME: 30 minutes	CALORIES: 710	SERVINGS: 1	CARBS: 52g	PROTEIN: 8g	FATS: 58g

INGREDIENTS:

- 1 small beet
- 1 cup mixed berries (strawberries, blueberries, and raspberries)
- 200ml canned coconut milk
- 1 teaspoon lemon juice
- 1 tablespoon maple syrup

INSTRUCTIONS:

1. Cut the beet into small chunks; place them in a saucepan and cover with water; bring to a boil, then reduce the heat and simmer for 20 minutes.
2. Combine the beet chunks, mixed berries, coconut milk, maple syrup and lemon juice in a blender.
3. Serve immediately.

FIG AND MAPLE SMOOTHIE

TOTAL TIME: 10 minutes	CALORIES: 426	SERVINGS: 1	CARBS: 84g	PROTEIN: 9g	FATS: 7g

INGREDIENTS:

- 5 figs
- 200ml whole milk
- 1 tablespoon maple syrup
- 1/2 banana
- 1 teaspoon vanilla extract
- A pinch of cinnamon for added warmth

INSTRUCTIONS:

1. If using dried figs, soak them in warm water for at least 30 minutes before blending.
2. Combine the figs, almond or whole milk, maple syrup, banana, cinnamon and vanilla extract in a blender.
3. Serve immediately.

SPINACH AND AVOCADO SMOOTHIE

TOTAL TIME: 10 minutes	CALORIES: 449	SERVINGS: 1	CARBS: 47g	PROTEIN: 12g	FATS: 28g

INGREDIENTS:

- 1 cup spinach leaves
- 1 avocado
- 200ml whole milk
- 1 small banana
- 1 tablespoon lemon juice

INSTRUCTIONS:

1. Combine the spinach leaves, avocado, whole milk, banana, and lemon juice in a blender.
2. Serve immediately.

CREAMY CARROT AND ORANGE SMOOTHIE

TOTAL TIME: 25 minutes	CALORIES: 310	SERVINGS: 1	CARBS: 57g	PROTEIN: 10g	FATS: 7g

INGREDIENTS:

- 2 medium carrots
- 200ml orange juice or 2 oranges
- 1/2 banana
- 200ml whole milk

INSTRUCTIONS:

1. Steam the peeled and chopped carrots for 15 minutes; allow to cool.
2. Squeeze the juice from the oranges until you have approximately 200ml.
3. Place the steamed carrots, orange juice, banana, and whole milk in a blender.
4. Serve immediately.

CHAPTER 7:
BONUSES

30-Day Meal Plan, Grocery List, Caregiver Toolkit, and 12 Soup Recipes

To gain access to the 30-Day Meal Plan, Grocery List, Caregiver Toolkit, and additional soup recipes, please scan the QR code below. This will take you to a website where you can enter your email, allowing me to send you the downloadable and printable PDFs.

Easy Guide to Scanning QR Codes with Your Smartphone

For iPhone:

1. **Open the Camera App:** Use the camera app on your device. You do not need to download a separate app.
2. **Point the Camera at the QR Code:** Hold your device so that the QR code appears in the viewfinder in the Camera app. Your device will recognize the QR code and a notification will appear.
3. **Access the Link:** Tap the notification that pops up to open the link associated with the QR code.

For Android:

1. **Open the Camera App:** Most modern Android phones can scan QR codes directly using the camera app.
2. **Point the Camera at the QR Code:** Align the QR code in the frame. Some devices may require you to tap a button to capture the code.
3. **Follow the Prompt:** Once the QR code is recognized, a link will appear or a notification will pop up. Tap on it to be taken to the corresponding content.

Made in the USA
Columbia, SC
30 October 2024

45350358R00061